With grateful

from

# SANDS OF SILENCE

*Derek H. Webster*

By the same author:

*The Abbot and the Dwarf*

DEREK WEBSTER

# Sands of Silence

## Tales of Wisdom from the Desert (2)

ST PAULS

ST PAULS
Middlegreen, Slough SL3 6BT, United Kingdom
Moyglare Road, Maynooth, Co. Kildare, Ireland

© ST PAULS 1993

ISBN 085439 460 5

Printed by Biddles Ltd, Guildford

ST PAULS is an activity of the priests and brothers of
the Society of St Paul who proclaim the Gospel through the
media of social communication

# Contents

*For my children*
*Sarah, Simon, Jeremy and Christopher*

# Preface

Some time ago I went to Israel to write a fairly academic book. Yet instead of inhabiting libraries and visiting archaeological sites, I was drawn for many months to desert places of deep quiet. In that stillness the stories of Abbot Nicholas and his disciple, John the Dwarf, were born. Though set within the tradition of fourth century monasticism, their stories seek to create space in contemporary lives. Perhaps their words are like a gap in the clouds – the gap between certainty and doubt, between a question and its solution, between noise and quiet, and between joy and grief. Walking the 'way' with them may raise a question:

> What
> does the traveller to your door
> ask, but that you sit down
> and share with him that
> for which there are no words?[1]

I have found much help in trying to understand and interpret my experience in the desert from the writings of poets and spiritual writers of several traditions. The bibliography indicates what has given most personal enrichment, though especial mention needs to be made of the contributions of Sr Benedicta Ward, Fr Norman Russell, Phyllis Tribble and Menrad Craighead.

During my writing of this book I have received an understanding and personal support from Wendy, my wife, which cannot adequately be put into words. Colleagues in the University of Hull have been endlessly stimulating and have shown a generous interest in my work, especially Alan, Joyce and Mike. My students have continued to teach me the importance of making that link between life and poetry without which our humanity is diminished. In the 1991-3 period I especially thank Duncan and Robert, Paul and Colin, Peter and Maddie, and reaching back to earlier times Patricia, Molly and Dean. The congregation and priests in St Peter's and St Francis' Churches, Cleethorpes, have shown a continuing encouragement – and patience – as I have tried many ideas out on them. I can never repay what I owe to Frs Brian, Tom, David and Ian as well as to Doreen and Margaret, John and Di, Janet and Piet, Betty and Keith, Ian and Pam, Barbara and Mary, and Kelly, Joan, Heather, Eric and Eddie. Each in his or her own way has helped me to remember. For:

> I had forgotten
>   the old quest for truth
>     I was here for.
> Other cares held me.[2]

In Israel I was able to resume that quest.

Special thanks go to Veronica Fraser, Director of Education in the Diocese of Worcester for her help and wisdom – and her vision in being able to see the big things in the small things.

In trying to reflect a Christian spirituality in stories, I am conscious of the huge debt I owe to so many other storytellers. They are too numerous to name and so much of what they say now rests in my own bones in ignorance of its source. Nevertheless I hope that I have not unwittingly infringed copyright or otherwise used material which others see as their own.

Throughout I have, apart from a single instance, used the Revised Standard Version of the Bible (Catholic Edition) for biblical quotations.

*Derek Webster*
The University of Hull
Feast of St Anselm, 1993

1. R.S. Thomas, Mass For Hard Times, Bloodaxe Books, 1992, p. 19.
2. R.S. Thomas, Later Poems, Macmillan, 1984, p. 60.

MEDITERRANEAN SEA

ALEXANDRIA • LAKE
MAREOTIS

NITRIA •

• CELLIA

WILDERNESS OF
SCETE

RIVER NILE

ARSINOE •

• PISPIR

• ANTINOE

EGYPT

Alexandria • Port Said
• Abu Mena
CAIRO ▣
Suez  Sinai
▽ Qattara
Depression
El Minya •
EGYPT
Red
Sea
Valley of the Kings •  • Thebes
• Luxor
Tropic of Cancer
S A H A R A
D E S E R T

# 1

# Time

Once Abbot Nicholas received two visitors. The first approached the courtyard to his cell in the darkness of early dawn. Dismounting a strong, young camel he asked permission to draw water from the well. It was Milesius, a merchant from Alexandria. Taking off a richly woven cloak, he allowed Nicholas to wash his feet. They then prayed for a short time before sitting together to eat a simple breakfast of salt bread and cheese served by John.

Nicholas lived very simply, with his disciple John the Dwarf, in the Nitrian deserts.[1] The credulous said that his holiness was so great that God had granted him the knowledge of all things: the wise saw his humility.

After the meal Milesius said to Nicholas:

'Holy Father, does the Lord God do well?'

Nicholas looked thoughtfully at him and said: 'He does, my son.'

The merchant was not satisfied. He said:

'But, Father have you not heard of the lowly brother who travelled these parts with his ass and his peacock? Darkness came before he had found any place to lodge. The oil in his lamp was almost gone. At last he stumbled across a small oasis where a caravan of travellers from the western desert rested for the night. Unruly men, they beat and robbed him, seizing his ass and peacock. He was thrust naked into the blackness of the desert night with no lamp.

In this the Lord God did not do well.'

Nicholas thought for a long time. At length he said to him:

'But who may tie the scroll of time?'

Then he blessed Milesius, bade John give him dates and wine for his journey and sent him away.

***

The second visitor arrived later in the morning. He was a wealthy physician called Agathon, who was travelling to Alexandria. He asked for water for his servants and camels as well as for himself. Nicholas washed his feet, prayed with him and offered figs to eat. In their talk together he asked the Abbot this question:

'Holy Father, does the Lord God do well?'

Nicholas gave the same reply: 'He does, my son.'

The physician looked disturbed. He said:

'But Father, have you not heard of the young monk who lived alone in the desert of Scete?[2] Attacked by brigands, his few possessions were taken and his cell destroyed. Thrown down an abandoned well, he lay unconscious for two days and nights before he could struggle free.

In this the Lord God did not do well.'

Nicholas looked at him and beyond him and slowly said:

'But who may tie the scroll of time?'

Then he blessed Agathon, told John to give him refreshment for his journey and sent him away.

***

John and Nicholas read the lessons for that hour.

> Oh, that I knew where I might find him,
> that I might come even to his seat!
> I would lay my case before him
> and fill my mouth with arguments.
>
> (Job 23:3-4)

After their prayers the Dwarf spoke quietly to his master. 'How can it be that God does well?'

The Abbot's eyes twinkled as he laughed softly and said: 'Would you accuse the Great One of wrong-doing, John?

Milesius the Merchant does not yet know that the lowly brother, treated so shamefully by the caravan of travellers, could struggle but a little distance away from the oasis which they held. Now, in the deepest part of the night when all was still, desert marauders fell upon those travellers and slew them all. Our brother was unnoticed for he no longer had an ass to greet the beasts used by these marauders. He had no peacock to betray his sad place of sojourn. Nor had he any lamp to draw their eyes to him.

Did God do well?

Agathon the Physician does not know that while the young monk of Scete lay unconscious hidden in the well, Caesar's soldiers came to conscript him as a slave to the Imperial Army. Seeing the destruction of his cell, they imagined him to be dead and moved away.

Did God do well?'

There was a long silence as the Abbot gazed into the vast emptiness of the desert. Then he said, almost in a whisper:

> 'It is not given to Milesius or Agathon or any human
> to tie the strings which bind the scroll of time.

Who can know the art which turns present into future?

Does a thief see the trap which the
householder has laid,
Or a viper the snare that is set for him?
May a mother who cradles twins
know the fleeting years
which have torment for her maid and
gladness for her son?
As a king may not foresee the richness of a
summer harvest,
neither will a beggar embrace death before his dying.

Yet to the Holy One, time gone, time now and
time to be, shine with the same light.
And for Him one beat of a locust's wing lasts
till all the hills of Lebanon bow to dust.
Only He is the Traveller who can follow both tracks
when the forest path divides.'

In this way did John the Dwarf catch within the form of
time the goodness of the One Who is Formless.

Therefore I have uttered what I did not understand,
things too wonderful for me which I did not know.

(Job 42:3)

# 2

# Sacrifice

*Sing to the Lord, for he has*
*triumphed gloriously;*
*the horse and his rider he has*
*thrown into the sea.*

(Exodus 15:21)

The Abbot and John had just finished their intercessions and readings for the late night prayer when they heard a quiet weeping. Together they went to the guest cells where the Lady Helena was staying with her servants. As the Feast of the Nativity of the Holy Child drew near, it was her custom to spend a brief time away from the world with Nicholas and his disciple. An elderly widow with large estates in Alexandria, she lived simply and gave most of her income to the poor of that great city. Her Christian faith was as robust as her questioning of it.

Dismissing her servants she invited Nicholas and John to sit with her. Her fine grey eyes were now free from tears, though there was a deep unease in her voice. She opened a scroll and said:

'I have heard of a baby boy who was born in Gilead. It was at that time before Israel had a king. He was the son of a common prostitute but was taken into his father's house. Now his father had a wife who bore him further sons. This baby grew to manhood in their company. As the father gathered the years within his life, his sons plotted against their half-brother. They said among themselves:

17

"Let us seize him and thrust him out of our father's house, lest the inheritance goes to one whose mother was a harlot."

So they abused him until he fled from them and went to live in the border country which is called the land of Tob. There he became a brigand and gathered to him many other wandering and dissolute men. He led them on raiding parties to the surrounding towns and soon they were greatly feared.

Now at this time the Ammonites made war on Israel and set their camp in Gilead. The elders of the tribe of Gilead were without an overlord, so they said: "Let us send to the land of Tob that the son of the harlot may lead us into battle. When they had spoken to him he derided them for their fickleness. Then he bargained with them saying:"If I lead you to victory over the Ammonites you must promise to make me your overlord in Gilead.' Such was their plight that they agreed to this.

First the son of the harlot tried to negotiate with the King of the Ammonites. When this failed he made preparations for battle. The Spirit of the Lord came to him and he made a promise to the High One. He said:

"If the Lord will give victory this day, whatsoever comes from my house to greet me when I return, shall be given to the Lord. It shall be sacrificed as a burnt offering."

In the battles that followed there was a great slaughter and twenty cities of the Ammonites were subdued. The Lord had given the enemies of Israel to the son of the harlot.

After this he came towards his home at Mizpah. His daughter, a young maiden of dark eyes and clear skin who loved her father dearly, was watching for his return. She was his only child and inhabited his heart. When she saw him at a distance, she decked herself in bright ribbons and taking timbrels joyously danced towards him with songs and laughter.

As he raised his eyes to his dwelling place, he saw only the one who lent delight to his life. In horror and anguish he interrupted her music and tore his clothing. Then he embraced her and declared to her his oath to the Lord. She lowered her look to the dust of the ground and said:

> "Do to me what you have vowed to the Lord God of Israel. But first permit me two months in which to wander the barren hills that I may lament my virginity with my companions."

He granted this and let her go for such a time. At its end she returned to him and he

> did with her according to his vow which he had made.
>
> (Judges 11:39)

So it was that a tradition was established that the young women of Israel mourned for the daughter of Jephthah the Gileadite, son of a harlot, for four days in each year.'[3]

Then the Lady Helena closed the scroll saying:

> 'So it is that to-night my sorrow is for a maiden who was the grand-daughter of a concubine. As I wept for my little sister, so was my weeping joined to that of a thousand generations.

Tell me. Did the Lord accept Jephthah's burnt offering?'

It was only after a long silence that John the Dwarf spoke.

'Upon the Word that is Truth rest the words that are written on a scroll. Catch beneath these words the whisper of the Spirit who is Love. Does He say:

When Pharoah's army was swept to destruction in the surging deep and Israel rejoiced, the Holy One wept at the drowning of his sons the Egyptians?[4]

When Samson pushed apart the pillars on which the Temple of Dagon rested and Israel exulted, the Lord God mourned the destruction of his children the Philistines?[5]

When Jephthah put forth his hand and took the spike, the Mighty One grieved at the violence done to a spotless virgin, victim of a father's faithless vow?'

Nicholas nodded and then said: 'What do we see?

A cord which binds the maiden to the altar's stone?
  Look again. That cord is Love.

A fire of myrtle and of lime which burns her breath
    away?
  Look again. That fire is Grace.

A life which, like water spilled upon the sands,
    may never be caught a second time?
  Look again. She dances among green herbs in a
    paradise of delight.

She asked of Him life.
  This He gave – everlastingly.'

\*\*\*

Then Abraham... took the knife to slay his son.
But... the Lord called to him from heaven... 'Do not
lay your hand on the lad.'

(Genesis 22:11-12)

# 3

# Glory

*Lo, he passes by me, and I see him not;*
*he moves on, but I do not perceive him.*

(Job 9:11)

Quickly John the Dwarf pulled open the gate of the
courtyard for the stranger. Already the fringes of the
sandstorm rushing from the east, whipped against his
skin. Stepping briskly into the cell a young man removed
his thick cloak and sat on a low stool. While Nicholas
washed his feet, he explained that he was travelling to
Alexandria on his family's business. A Roman by birth,
his name was Tullus. It was clear that he could not
continue his journey until the storm had blown itself out.

After a simple meal of salt bread, herbs and water,
Nicholas and John prepared for the prayers and readings
of the hour. Although Tullus declined to share their worship, they noted how carefully he attended to the words
they spoke.

> So the Lord God caused a deep sleep to fall upon
> the man, and while he slept took one of his ribs...
> and the rib... he made into a woman.

> ... the Lord God called to the man, and said to him,
> 'Where are you?'

(Genesis 2:21-22; 3:9)

When they had finished Tullus, looking puzzled, said to
John:

'Is your God a common thief that He steals a man's rib?'

The Dwarf laughed in his gentle way and replied:

'Is he a thief who takes water but gives wine;
who seizes a fist of sand but bestows a ring of gold?

    Thus did Adam receive Eve.'

But Tullus was not to be so quickly put off his argument. He shook a head of brown curls at John and said:

'If your God is not a thief, why did he wait for Adam's sleep and nature's dark to do this deed?'

John smiled and said:

'A king, drinking the rarest of his wines,
does not recall the asses' dung which sustained his
    vine,
or the feet of farmers' sons that pressed his grapes.
Nor did Adam seek to witness Eve's creation.'

Still deeply dissatisfied Tullus said:

Your God lacks knowledge for he says to Adam, "Where art thou?" Why? Did He not know the place where he stood?'

Then Nicholas spoke quietly:

'God's Holy Word is eternal.
Each age, each generation, and each person is
    embraced by it.
So God says to us:
    "Where are you within the span of time I have
        given for you?"
In this way He prompts us to reflect the glory
    with which He has surrounded us on earth'.

Tullus paused but could find no foothold in such an answer.

'What is glory? Where is it? I do not understand', he said.

Nicholas looked thoughtfully at him and answered very slowly.

'Glory is the radiance of His Living Presence.

See Him in
New light filling the valleys at each dawning,
Trackless meadows deserted by their flocks,
Strange islands set in the mists of the
    western seas.

Hear Him in
The minstrelsy of bees' wings,
The silent cry of a mute child,
Crack of briar and apple-wood in spring fires.

Feel Him in
The trembling heartbeat of a sparrow's young,
The play of rain and ocean's sporting waves,
The hand-held lock of lovers' leavings.

Remember that
When what is, is most truly; it is girdled
    with Glory.
The tree in summer's prosperity, a bear on
    Hermon's peak,
Evening's gold-copper sun, a flock of
    yellow marigolds,
All bear His Love.

So gashed rocks and deep pools, ants astir and
    crickets hopping are His saints'.

There was a pause, then Nicholas smiled and said:

'Perhaps one day you will hear his voice in the wind asking,

"Tullus, where art thou?"'

When the storm was finished and John and Nicholas had set their visitor on his way again, the Dwarf said to his Master:

'Will his eyes be opened?'

Nicholas looked far out into the wastes for some time before speaking. Then he said:

'It is small advantage for eyes to see
    if the heart is blind.
The great world brims over with His Glory,
    yet He may only dwell
where a person chooses to give Him entrance.

Is not the cloth that is to be dyed, first carefully
    prepared?
Do not soldiers before a battle, first learn their drills?
So may the path Tullus takes slowly show him
    that Glory
which a voice may not say,
    for it is beyond all speech, all words.'

Once again it was time for the prayers and Scripture readings.

Declare his glory among the nations,
his marvellous works among all the peoples!
For great is the Lord, and greatly to be praised.
                            (1 Chronicles 16:24-25)

# 4

# Wife

*A good wife who can find?...*
*Charm is deceitful, and beauty is vain,*
*but a woman who fears the*
*Lord is to be praised.*

(Proverbs 31:10.30)

It puzzled John that the slight figure coming towards him was so ill-equipped for journeying in the desert. He was even more surprised to find that it was a woman who travelled the Nitrian wastes alone. As he helped her across the small courtyard to one of the guest cells, he could see that she was almost exhausted.

Nicholas joined him and together, with discretion and tenderness, they met the needs of their guest. But both saw the marks of a branding iron on her wrists. She slept for a day and a night before rising to refresh herself.

In the cool of the new morning the Abbot and the Dwarf listened as she spoke quietly.

'I am Aisha, slave to the house of the Lord Melqart. His caravans carry dyed cloth from Phenice to the great cities of the east.[6] Since childhood I have served his family. My Lord's beard is now white, yet last year he took the beautiful maiden Estarta, to be his wife. I am her chief servant and have charge of her wardrobe. In this service I have learned the secrets of her heart.'

She paused to sip water. A woman no longer young, she spoke good Greek and had the air of one used to taking responsibility and discharging it intelligently. She raised her eyes, it seemed, to what lay beyond the Abbot and his disciple and whispered:

'My Lord's house is set in a fine park with scented grasses and peacocks. It was tended by the slave Anaxus. Though but twenty summers, he pruned and planted with skill and wisdom and pleased the Lord Melqart with his work. He also pleased the Lady Estarta – though with his strength and comeliness.

When my Lord last took his caravan to trade, she walked in the gardens to request of him honeysuckle and lilac for her bedroom. Bringing the choicest blossoms to the house, he found her upon her bed, perfumed and in veils. She bade him be with her, but he would not.

Three times in three days she pressed him to lie with her upon her couch. Three times, with quiet courtesy and proper deference, he refused. He would not entertain this evil against his Master.

On the night of the fourth day, she went in secret to his room whilst he was still asleep, and tried to lie with him. He awoke and sought to rise from his pallet. As he did so, she clutched at his tunic and tore it from his chest. He fled naked into the garden. But there was none to see, none to hear, what had happened.

When the Lord Melqart returned, the Lady Estarta feigned great distress. She complained that Anaxus had entered her room unbidden at night. In her struggle against him, she claimed to have torn his tunic. But, she said, he had borne her down, forcing her to lie with him. She showed the torn garment, which she said he had left in her room.

My Lord was deep with an anger which overcame his reason. He ordered Anaxus to be put in chains. Then he sent for the executioner of Phenice. In an hour, Anaxus' body lay among all that city's rubbish. His bloody head was given to the Lady Estarta. She crowned it with a cunning garland of purple lilac and yellow honeysuckle – then she spat upon it.'

The last words were uttered with silent breath. She wept quietly. After a pause her story was finished quickly:

'Such was my respect for my Master, such was my sorrow for Anaxus, such was my hate for the Lady Estarta, that I could no longer remain in that house. I ran away.'

John and Nicholas could see that she was again exhausted. She rested and did not speak further until the evening.

\*\*\*

Now Joseph was taken down to Egypt, and Potiphar... bought him... And after a time his master's wife cast her eyes upon Joseph, and said, 'Lie with me.'

(Genesis 39:1.7)

As Nicholas and John finished their readings for that hour, they noticed Aisha moving in the courtyard. They went out to her. She spoke:

'It is not fitting that I should remain here. At day's dawn I will journey again – and for ever. There is no healing for my spirit.'

Then Nicholas said:

'Your grief for Anaxus is a song which shivers the heart. For now his fingers pluck strings which you may not hear, his limbs gladden to melodies which you may not catch, and his eyes see what you cannot behold.

Yet your love does not die in his dying. Ponder
   His heed for blazing crocus and fledgling lark,
   His anguish over fallen oak and crushed pear,
   His faith in green life which pulses beyond death.

Let your life extend his heed, his care and his faith. In such a way will your life create for his life.

So your solitude will not turn to bitter loneliness. So you may give birth to what honours your son Anaxus.'

She remained motionless and he went on:

'Like waves on the seashore of unmeasured worlds,
Your sadness for Melqart crushes the heart.
   Yet Spring
      Brings green array for naked branch,
      Hoists sails of new-cast butterfly, and
      Opens lovers' eyes for tender looks.

Let the knot which pulls your days take time to ease.
Let life approach that season when pardon grows.
So may the seed which fell to corruption rise
   to greenness.
So may be nurtured what can forgive Melqart, father
   to your son.'

***

As the distant figure of Aisha was caught by the sands, and Master and Disciple returned to their cell to prepare for the prayers and readings, John said slowly,

'What grief now strikes at Lord Melqart's heart who in needless jealousy executed his own son?'

# 5

# Values

*So, therefore, whoever of you does not renounce
all that he has cannot be my disciple.*

(Luke 14:33)

John was aware that the stranger was taking no part in
the Synaxis.[7]

> 'This bread that I break, it is His Body.
> Is it not fractured for all?
>
> This wine that I pour, it is His Blood.
> Is it not spilled for all?
>
> This bread and this wine, do they not draw
> the poor things of the earth to us?'

While it was yet dark, John and Nicholas had journeyed
some distance to the cells of neighbouring brothers living in the Nitrian wastes. It was their habit to meet early
each Sabbath day to celebrate, pray and break their fast
together.

Tall and middle-aged, the stranger had obviously rested
in one of the guest cells overnight. John caught his silent,
questioning eyes and watched as they carefully searched
the face of each brother present. After the worship and
their simple meal, he spoke.

> 'Holy fathers of the desert, you who fear
> Neither wind nor sun,
> Scorpion's sting nor bush's thorn,

Is there knowledge among you of one who
    came as young
To these drear wastes three decades past.
A Greek by birth, his name was Lycias.'

All was strangely silent for some time. Finally a brother
whom John could not properly see, such was the fierce-
ness of the sun's light behind his head, asked in a thin,
calm voice:

'What business would you have with him?'

'I come to bid him receive his inheritance and have
charge of great estates in Corinth.'

'He would laugh at such an earthly inheritance,
    for he has a greater, which is heavenly.'

'I come to bid him leave this loneliness
    for fellowship with the lords of his city.'

'He would mock such company for in solitude he is
    made one with all men.'

'I come to bid him return to a mother, crooked
      with years,
    whose eyes seek him before their final closing.'

'He would say his mother is,
    Sheltering palms, bread which feeds,
    Renewing Spirit, Word Who lives.'

Through the stillness the stranger persisted, saying
finally,

'I would bid him embrace a wife, already grey,
    and a son now grown to manhood.'

'He would whisper that while he is possessed of
    the High One,

In such a light and fire, he embraces all.'

After a long pause the same brother spoke again.

'I knew this Lycias whom you seek.
He was in Scete's great wilderness, though now
   he is dead.
Return to Corinth with this news.
Give the inheritance to his son.
Let him be merciful and do kindly to the women.'

***

As they started back for their cells, the Abbot and John
were joined by the stranger. The first part of his journey
took the same direction as theirs. Before leaving he had
talked privately with the hermit who had known Lycias
in Scete and confirmed his identity. The stranger's name
was Photius. A younger brother to Lycias, on their father's death, he had been charged to seek him out because of the inheritance. Now he was deeply saddened.

Nicholas spoke to him and told a story to bring understanding.

'I heard of a fool from the deserts who went into a
strange city. Its tongue was unknown to him.

While guards dozed in the sun's heat, he wandered
through the king's palace. "What a splendid house
is prepared for me", he thought.

Then he came to the royal robing room. "What
magnificent clothes are laid out for me", he said.

In regal attire, he walked into the banqueting hall
which was prepared for the King's birthday feast.
"What a sumptuous supper is set for me", he re-
marked.

Eventually he was discovered and seized by the king's guards. "How fortunate I am to walk with men of such eminence", he thought.

Brought before the king for judgement, he said, "Even the most distinguished in this city talk with me."

In chains and cast into the darkness of the king's dungeon, he was overjoyed. In an ecstasy his soul sang this song:

> "At last, within this safe lodging, I may make
>     my journey.
> In this darkness my soul is protected from
>     distraction.
> Stale bread and sour water subdue my appetites.
> Tokens around my hands and feet discipline
>     my body.
> Thus my holy friends have prepared me for the
>     kiss off the One who is Infinite Love."

What do you think, is this fool alive or dead?'

*** 

As Photius turned towards the north and left them, John said, 'Why did Lycias lie?'

Smiling a little Nicholas replied, 'Did he lie? For is he not dead?'

After a little while they stopped to say the psalms and readings for that time.

> Likewise, my brethren, you have died to the law through the body of Christ, so that you may belong to one another, to him who has been raised from the dead in order that we may bear fruit for God.

> (Romans 7:4)

# 6

# Brother

*... He met Jehonadab... and he greeted him, and
said to him, 'Is your heart true to my heart as mine
is to yours?' And Jehonadab answered, 'It is.'
Jehu said, 'If it is, give me your hand.' So he gave
him his hand.*

(2 Kings 10:15)

Nicholas had lain in the ever-tightening claw of his cruel
fever for five days. It had first visited him on a pilgrim-
age to Jerusalem. Now John noticed how its grip in-
creased with the frailty of age. Deeply unconscious, the
Abbot's breath fluttered lightly and his skin turned to
ivory.

John helped the traveller who had just arrived with his
camels, and then showed him into one of the guest cells.
The lamps were lit and bread, cheese and figs with fresh
water brought. The Dwarf explained that his master's
sickness would slacken the hospitality he could give.

The visitor was a young man whose dark eyes showed
concern as John spoke of Nicholas' illness. From the
music of his tongue and the rich brown of his skin, John
guessed that he came from lands to the east of the Euphra-
tes. He said to the Dwarf:

> 'I have some knowledge of medicine, for my teacher
> Jani healed many in the cities on the Indus River.
> May I visit your master?'

Through all the night John helped as the young man took
a small box from his satchel, and distilled a sweet smell-
ing liquid. With great skill he passed a soft tube down the

35

Abbot's throat and poured the potion into his stomach. Then he mixed oils and crushed herbs to make an embrocation with which he anointed Nicholas' body. Finally he blew a fine powder into his nostrils. As they waited, the young man dozed and John, in gloomy sadness, whispered the psalms for that time.

> They say, 'A deadly thing has fastened upon him;
>> he will not rise again from where he lies'...
>>> but the Lord takes thought for me.
>> Thou art my help and my deliverer; do not tarry.
>>> O my God!
>>>> (Psalm 41:8; 40:17)

At dawn consciousness returned. And with each hour of that day Nicholas slowly improved. Though very weak, he insisted that John sit him up so that he could meet their guest. As he watched his master, John's spirit rejoiced. Youth and age embraced as the Abbot and the young man spoke eagerly of those mountain passes and broad rivers, of those great cities and empty deserts each had travelled.

Then the young man moved towards the door of the cell and said:

'Now is the time for my prayer.'

'Does your prayer draw a circle which can include us?' asked Nicholas thoughtfully, as he glanced at John.

The young man stared at them with an understanding which seemed to have been born from a thousand years of wisdom, then nodded.

So it was that the Abbot and the Dwarf sat with their hearts open as the dusky young man intoned his chants in an ancient language. Its music was unintelligible to them, though they felt its power.

36

He paused for some time at the end and then turned and said:

> 'We have prayed to the One:
>> Who, resting in a single place, lodges
>>> in every place.
>> Who, fleeing before the wind, never moves.
>> Who, without name or identity, is known in
>>> all oceans, and each blade of pasture.
>
> To the One not attained by instruction or learning,
>> Who is hidden in the heart,
>>> as oil in a sesame seed,
>>> as butter in a skin of cream,
>>> or water in a secret spring.
>
> Behold, this One is encountered
>> before thought arises,
>> before distinctions appear,
>> before contradictions occur.
>
> We have asked for:
>> mercy on those who are oppressed,
>> guidance to those who are lost, and
>> healing for those who are sick.'

After they had fed the camels and eaten a little themselves, the young man spoke to John and Nicholas before departing.

He gave them a small phial of medicine with instructions for its use. Pausing a little, he looked at Nicholas and then said carefully:

> 'Though I may pray with you, is it not forbidden for you to pray with me?'

'Once', said Nicholas, 'there was a king who wished to learn from a sage of the forest. He had him brought to his palace and commanded him to declare the secret of his wisdom. The sage refused. Three times the king asked.

Three times he was refused. In great anger the king insisted – else death would follow. So the sage went up to a servant of the king and whispered in his ear. The servant remained in his position and did nothing. Enraged the king ordered the same servant to seize the sage, which he did immediately. At this the sage burst out laughing and said:

'When I ordered your servant to seize you, he continued in his place unmoving; when you ordered him to take me, this he did quickly. Why?'

'Because he knows that from childhood, I have been prepared for kingship and have now taken its authority.'

'Exactly', said the sage smiling. 'And so before you can take the authority which the secret of wisdom gives, you must prepare yourself over many years.'

After a pause Nicholas continued:

'John and I are like this king and servant. We are not tuned to the whisper of wisdom which you teach. We serve another.

Can a single egg sit in the nest of hawk and swan? Can spider's web and toad's tongue snare the same summer fly?

As childhood is single and may not be spent twice over, so each person inhabits only the forest which nurtured him'.

The young man inclined his head in assent before saying:

'Yet do not myrtle and birch, in burning, give equal warmth? Is not each enamelled colour of the rainbow of equal beauty? Will not the milk from either breast quiet the crying babe?'

As John and Nicholas watched the young man's camels
carry him in to the wastes of Nitria, the Abbot said:

'Where two faiths weave a wisdom
    which clothes its servants in truth,
Where two faiths ungird a Love
    that makes its home in believers' hearts,
Do both reflect He Who is beyond
    the saying of either?'

# 7

# Presence

Young Xoius saw them first. With joy he ran to give a greeting. But the long journey through the Nitrian wastes to Pispir had bled Nicholas' strength.[8] John helped the lad and they set the Abbot on a pallet in the guest's cell. The frail, old man was guardian for the souls of Xoius, Hierax and Spyridon. They lived among those other solitaries whose cells clenched the sands of Pispir.

It was not until the following morning that Nicholas was well enough to embrace Xoius. Before breaking the night fast the three of them said their prayers and read the Holy Scriptures.

'For inquire, I pray you, of bygone ages,
and consider what the fathers have found;
for we are but of yesterday, and know nothing,...
  Will they not teach you?'

(Job 8:8-10)

\*\*\*

After this Xoius spoke in a quiet and serious manner to the Abbot of his life and trials at Pispir.

As John listened it seemed to him that this brother sang a bitter psalm.

'Each day thoughts swarm like bees.
Each day barbs sting and wound, for
Each day I see I have no love for God.

How may I adore a Beauty, invisible to my sight?
How can I cherish a Word whose sound is that
of silence?

How will I faint with desire for the touch of
    an Intangible?
Shall I catch the scent of spikenard on One
    without odour?[9]
Will my tongue caress and taste Who is
    without savour?'

Nicholas waited a while, then said:

'My son, what brings love to your soul?'

Xoius smiled. In answering he spoke softly as if he
enfolded in his arms, all sleeping, his very life's delight.

'Holy Father, they are only those things which
    gladden all hearts.

My eyes love
    Soundless spiders whose silver nets adorn my cell,
    Sky and sands in whose circuit my life is set,
    Sight of kneeling brothers seeking soul's bread.

My ears love
    Swirl of egrets' wings and sparrows' quarrels,
    Dawn's quiet breath and rolling storm in all
      her wrath,
    Song and psalm as brothers say their praises.

I love the touch
    Of sharpness in a thorn's fierce point,
    Of wet from darkling clouds and dry from
      passioned sun,
    Of brothers' arms in peace's generous embrace.

I love the scent
    Of withered leaves and herbs all fresh,
    Of humbled dust and marsh's drying mud,
    Of brothers' breath as joy and mirth ring
      their hearts.

I love the taste
  Of desert berries, figs and cheese,
  Of spring's new torrent and night's clear air,
  Of bread and wine upon my tongue, giving life.

  But in all of this I have no love for God.'

*\*\**

At this point they rested their conversation and prayed together. Nicholas read from the Book of Job.

By the breath of God ice is given...
  He loads the thick cloud with moisture, ...
Can you, like him, spread out the skies,
  hard as a molten mirror?
                        (Job 37:10.11.18)

Then the Abbot took Xoius outside the cell and walking with him said:

'Once there was a wealthy merchant who had a dearly loved son. While he was away in another town, his son became sick and forgot who he was. He did not even remember the beautiful gardens through which he walked as his special pleasure. He wandered far from home. Though the merchant's servants searched the great cities of the land, the son could not be found. Then he said to himself:

  'Without my son, my wealth brings no happiness. I shall use it to create many gardens in
  the land such as my son loved.'

And this he did.

Now one day the son, in a far city, walked through one of his father's newly planted gardens. A joy overwhelmed him. The sight of almond blossom and shrill cry of proud peacocks, the smell of jonquils and strawberries' taste, the touch of soft earth, slackened a little the chain that held his mind. Then he said to himself:

> 'This passing joy is but a shadow of that greater joy which endures forever. I shall seek the one who created such a garden. In time I may find a greater beauty from which this lesser beauty springs'.

So his search began.

Dear Xoius,

> You love soil and clouds,
>     so does He who fashions them.
> You love pelicans and crickets,
>     so does He who creates them.
> You love the brethren,
>     so does He who died for love of them.
>
> You and He are twin in love.
> Let all He bestows ravish your soul.
> In time you will discern His print upon it.'

***

'Will Xoius find the Father in His creation?' asked John later, when he and Nicholas were alone.

'If he does', whispered the Abbot, seeming to speak to himself, 'his journey will then take him on through another wilderness, where there are no trees and sands burn, a wilderness of deep darkness and gloomy desolation, where there is no refreshment.'

# 8
# Lovers

*Rachel was beautiful and lovely.*
*Jacob loved Rachel.*
(Genesis 29:17-18)

John listened hard. He could hear, through the quietness of the morning air, the whispered singing of an amorous Egyptian song. It had been popular in the taverns of Alexandria half a century ago. He looked at Nicholas, who was smiling broadly.

It stopped as they approached Spyridon's cell. Gaunt with fasting and heavy with years, he welcomed them gladly. 'My bones stick fast', he piped, as the Abbot and the Dwarf knelt to read God's Words and pray with him. All that he could now do was lean his frail, tiny body against the wall of the cell.

My beloved speaks and says to me:
   'Arise... my fair one, and come away;
     for lo, the winter is past...
The flowers appear on the earth...
   and the voice of the turtledove
     is heard in our land.'
(Song of Songs 2:10-12)

\*\*\*

After his confession and a long, private conversation with Nicholas who guarded his soul, Spyridon set a simple meal for them all. As they ate John noticed his joy and the light which flared in his eyes. So did Nicholas.

'You have welcomed us as brothers with love and friendship', said the Abbot lightly, 'but I think that it is not we who bring today's happiness for you.'

Spyridon gazed at the floor and only after some time said very simply:

'It was on this day, three score years ago, that first I met the Christ. Will you hear my story?'

They nodded agreement. Reaching to a shelf, he took from its corner a small pouch. Within was a cheap metal ring. He put it on as he spoke.

'For the first twenty years of my life, before I followed the desert path, I lived in Alexandria. My father was a skilled potter. He taught me the art of decorating his work. Each week we sold our vases in the great bazaar of that city. On an evening, as we finished trading, it was a custom for us to go to a nearby inn for cheap wine and fish.

On my natal day of nineteen years, I sat alone at the tavern's table. My father had stayed to bargain with a caravan of merchants. Wine was brought to me and I raised my head to meet that love which now enfolds all my days.

> Torn clothes, split sandal, grimed arm;
> Honey skin, apple's breath, shining hair;
> We looked – and understood.
> Our eyes gave veiled consent.
> So my beloved gave entrance for Christ
> In sad leper, crying widow, orphaned child,
> And bids me care for Him in them.

> My beloved sang with six-stringed psaltery
> A bawdy song of broken vows and passions rude.
> But we pledged to eternity with a wordless 'Yes'.

So my beloved gave entrance for Christ
In sad captives chained by darkness,
And bids me sit with Him in them.

Steps turn to tiny attic.
Dream-like face, hidden things shyly revealed.
'I am my beloved's
And my beloved is mine.'
So my beloved gave entrance for Christ
In all longings and fire of bodies' passions,
And bids me hear Him in them.

My beloved was buried on Sunday.
No Grecian statue to register the tumbling hair,
Beauteous limbs, lips all set to please.
Did sickness ever boast so perfect a victim?
So my beloved gave entrance for Christ
In all who die unmourned, unseen,
And bids me unite myself to Him in them.

For a year I carried the beloved's face in my heart. Then
Brother Isaac brought the Holy Word of God to those
who traded in the bazaar. It was he who taught me to see
within and behind that face, another Face which is Beauty
Itself. Then he brought me to these wastes and showed
me the desert way.

The song that I sang as you came this morning was that
sung in the tavern on my natal day of so many years ago.
I wear a ring from that day, given by Christ as He
ravished my soul with love and bound me to Him with
thongs of mercy and peace.'

The pitch of Spyridon's joy brought tears of love for his
Divine Master. Then he reminded them that it was time
again for them to say their prayers.

Hark! my beloved is knocking...
I opened to my beloved,
but my beloved had turned and gone.
... I sought... I called...
(Song of Songs 5:2.6)

\*\*\*

During the night Brother Spyridon's sleep passed into everlasting life. His sickness was so brief that no-one was even aware of it.

The brothers asked the Abbot what to do. Nicholas said:

'Let him be wrapped in his cloak, it is an old friend which has served for many years.

But let two holes be cut in it that his arms may rest outside. He may thus the quicker embrace that Lord whom he has loved and served for three score years.

Let the palms of his hands be open. He brought nothing into the world and he takes nothing out.

Place his ring on a thumb. With it a rose of Sharon opened scented petals for him in his youth. With it that Lord who loves all, betrothed Himself to him and brought him to the desert. He now takes him to His secret arbour to drink the new wine of the pomegranates.'

And these things were done.

# 9
# Growth

Hierax wept. The old Abbot waited silently. Then the brother whispered:

'Holy Father. My darkness is very great. My tongue does not match the thoughts of my heart.'

In deepest misery Hierax, now in the prime of his years, walked with Nicholas through the wastes around Pispir one morning. The Abbot guarded his soul and was determined not to leave until they had spoken of a serious matter.

> 'I lie by the sea's shore, but feel no spray.
> I rest in the hills, but see no glory.
> I recite the prayers: they have no sense.
> I read the Scriptures: their power fades.
>
> My spirit is the sullen smoke of a dampened fire.
> The Holy One no longer abides with me.'

Hierax spoke haltingly of his desolation. Nicholas gently held his arm. Then they broke their talk to say the prayers and readings for that time.

> So when the woman saw that the tree... was to be desired to make one wise, she took of its fruit and ate; and she also gave some to her husband. Then the eyes of both were opened... therefore the Lord God sent him forth from the garden of Eden... He drove out the man.
>
> (Genesis 3:6.7.23.24)

'Thus has God driven me from His Presence', whispered Hierax.

Nicholas thought for some time then asked him:

'How many gates need a man walk through to understand this Scripture?'

'But one – if it is the right one. Though are there not seventy more if the first should fail?'

'Exactly', said Nicholas. 'Here is a gate.

> Once there was a rich king who loved his only son with a great but very foolish love. From the prince's birth he created within his palace and its gardens, such splendour for him that his eyes and ears would see and hear only the most beautiful sights and sounds. He built a high wall all around and forbade his son to climb it and learn of the evil on its other side. But as the son grew older, it was just this that he wished to do and know. Finally in secret one night, the young man climbed a ladder. He got to the top of the wall and looked over. But in doing this he stretched too far, slipped and fell back into the garden. Severely injured the king's physicians yet managed to save him – though never again would he move from his bed, speak any words, hear any sounds or see any sights. At last his father the king had his son for ever within his garden.

Is the Lord God like this?'

'Of course not,' said Hierax. 'By chance the foolish king achieves what he desires. But the Lord God witnesses what he does not desire.'

Then Nicholas said, 'Yet think.

Do not both the Lord God and this king, in seeking to restrain a son from the pain of knowledge, prompt him to seek it?

Can you allow this thought? Before the fruit was eaten,

before the fruit was plucked, before the serpent questioned Eve, the Lord God planted the forbidden tree. In that very planting, was not innocence lost and were not Eve with Adam driven from Eden?

Every question "Why?" also asks "Why not?"

Hierax looked very puzzled. They paused to pray and read together as was the custom of each at that time.

> Noah was a righteous man... Noah walked with God...

> So he said, 'I am Abraham's servant...' he said to me, 'The Lord before whom I walk, will send his angel with you...'
>                                    (Genesis 6:9; 24:34.40)

During their worship together Hierax' sadness had returned. He looked at the Abbot and said very simply: 'I no longer walk with God.'

Again Nicholas took time to answer. 'You open the wrong gate. Here is another.

> Once there was a good king who had two sons, one was much younger than the other. He loved them both with a deep and a wise love. The younger he kept with him throughout each day as he taught him the skill of kingly government. The elder he sent before him to the courts of justice to practice judgement among the people.

So does the Lord God walk with those who take childish steps and guards them lest they stumble. So does the Lord God place before Him those who are mature. No longer do they need the sight and touch of Him. Now they walk with faith and trust in the way that He has set for them.'

***

Some hours later they finished their communion with each other. Hierax knew now the direction in which he should walk. Before he left the Abbot, who was near to exhaustion, the brother said:

'Pray for me that
    As I leave the green meadow for a barren place;
    As I forsake the clack of crows for a dark quiet;
    As I cast off a lily's scent for dull staleness;
    As I yield platter of new bread for bitter herbs;
    As I leave petals' softness for stinging thistle;
      I may find Him in blackness and pain, in
          emptiness and doubt.'

'He awaits you', said Nicholas, 'though at the end of your journey. Now is the time to begin. The valley is steep, the light gone, the air stinking, yet He bids you walk before Him. Only those who can enter this dark night will reach the embrace of His Love.'

I kept my faith, even when I said,
    'I am greatly afflicted';
    I walk before the Lord.
            (Psalm 116:10.9)

# 10

# Apple Tree

*Thus says the Lord God:*
*'I will take a sprig from the lofty top of the cedar...*
*and I myself will plant it upon a high... mountain...*
*that it may bring forth boughs and bear fruit...*
*and under it will dwell all kinds of beasts;*
*in the shade of its branches birds of every sort will nest.*

(Ezekiel 17:22.23)

The cell was empty, though footprints led towards some trees growing among desert grasses about a mile away. Nicholas and John were seeking shelter from the sun's flames as they journeyed from Pispir back to the Nitrian wastes.

Approaching the oasis, they noticed how carefully tended it was. A brother drew from a spring of fresh water. Then, as if mindful of a cherished possession, he gently moistened the roots of a young apple tree. In the middle of his years, Brother Mark was a small but sturdy man, whose skin was burned nut brown. He greeted them with openness and love, as if they were natural kin to him.

After he had washed their feet and they had prayed together, he bade them rest beneath the shade of a date palm. Then he returned to his cell to bring bread with cheese and figs. As they ate he told them that he had followed the desert path in this place for thirty summers.

'Will you speak to us of what the Holy One has revealed to you in this time?' asked the Abbot, gazing directly into Mark's eyes.

He was silent for a long time. Then with a transparent spirit he said:

'Twice my Father has visited to bestow His teaching. After ten summers walking the desert way, during a night when I fell into a deep sleep, He entered my cell. Taking me in His arms He set me down under sun and clouds in a green garden. Then He said:

"Take my only treasure. Plant it at the centre of the garden".

He took from Himself a seed and handed it to me with great tenderness.

Now within this garden were hidden grottos and spacious lawns, fluting birds and running creatures. Its many paths skirted stony pools and wreathed rose arbours. But at its centre was a dark barrenness. Here I planted the seed. And from it grew an apple tree which dazzled me with all the colours of light. As I looked away I saw that it embraced the nakedness of a beauteous young man. Then, light as the wind he stepped through all the scent and sound of the garden and was lost amid its maze of tracks.

I sought his presence in all the abundance of that mysterious place.

He was not in falling water or flower's bell,
Not under brown stone or honey's comb,
Not in squirrel's cleft or hollow of bird's wing.
He was not in secret cave or unbroken egg.

In sadness I returned to my apple tree. It was blackened and split .

"Who has done this?" I cried.
"None but thou," came answer back.

Then I awoke from my sleep.

53

After another ten summers walking the desert way, He came to me again. I was in a deep sleep in my cell when once more He took me in His arms and set me below a bleak hill. In that drear place only creatures of the dark stalked their helpless prey. None but the bittern shrieked her lonely cry.

Upon the hill stood my darkling apple tree. It held in tight embroidery of death the naked body of the beauteous young man. As the white milk of the fig flows quickly when its fruit is snapped, so all life was spilled from Him.

"Why was this done?" I cried.
"Thou hast required it", came answer back.

My soul could bear to watch no longer. But as I looked away I saw a consuming fire surround the apple tree. From its dust was fashioned a seed of myrrh. This seed was carried away by a strong bird. Again I sought the young man to anoint his body's piercings and bind him for burial. But I could not find him.

He was not among the tentacles of sea's forests,
Nor snow of high mountains.
He was not among the empty shadows of
    the wilderness,
Nor the dryness of human hearts.

Then I awoke from my sleep.'

The three sat in silence for some time.

'And now, at the end of your third decade of years on the desert path, you prepare this place perchance He will visit again?' asked the Abbot.

Mark nodded.

'During this season I sleep in hope. I pray that at His coming He will show me where the bird has buried the seed of myrrh.

Perhaps it is to become the apple tree of the New Jerusalem. Perhaps it is to stand by a river flowing from His
Throne.[10] Perhaps under its canopy the young man will
be robed in glory.'

*\*\*\**

The Abbot and the Dwarf had been walking for about
two hours, when John looked back to the oasis. He asked
Nicholas:

'Will the Holy One come again to Brother Mark?'

A wisp of a smile passed over the Abbot's face as he
said:

> 'How may He who is eternally present,
>    absent Himself?
> How may He who is heard in each sound,
>    silence Himself?
>  How may He who is in all motion,
>    still Himself?
> How may the One whose being is love,
>    cease from loving?
>
>> What we are told in dreams
>> is already deeply set within our souls.'

Soon they stopped to read the Scripture for the time of
day.

> As an apple tree among the trees of the wood,
>    So is my beloved among young men...
> Who is that coming up from the wilderness
>    Leaning upon her beloved?
> Under the apple tree I awakened you.
>
>> (Song of Songs 2:3; 8:5)

# 11
# Riches

Home. As they pushed open the door of their cell, the intruder sprang out before them. He put a long knife to their throats. Nicholas and John had never been attacked by robbers in all their years in the desert. They knew that the poor and destitute often preyed on merchants and rich travellers who journeyed through Nitria. But usually the bandits were aware that monks were even poorer than themselves.

'Give me your gold', he hissed.

Nicholas replied with a deep stillness in his voice:

'Take it. Yet say,
How will you ascend the sky to touch its burning rose?
That is all the gold we have.'

'Give me your silver', he bellowed.

'Take it. Yet say,
How will you carry away the only light of night?
That is all the silver we have.'

'Give me your gems', he screeched.

'Take them. Yet say.
How will you persuade each rainbow tint to stay?
These are all the gems we have.'

Give me your wealth', he howled.

'Take it. Yet say,
How will you capture earth and sky, and all therein?
That is all the wealth we have.'

'Give me what you treasure', he wailed.

'He is already yours, if you receive Him.
His body is bread for you. His blood is wine for you.
We hold no greater treasure than the Christ.'

Then the robber paused. At last he understood the total poverty of the two tired figures standing before him. Looking at the gauntness of the malformed midget and the pitiable frailty of the old Abbot, he saw that neither could endanger him. Though strangely he also felt that neither feared him.

Before he could speak again John said in a calm and friendly way:

'We see from the dust on your cloak and the sod of your sandals, that you have travelled far. Let us prepare a meal for you and wash the stings of Nitria from your feet.'

Warily he agreed to receive these services.

As Nicholas washed his feet, the robber stretched out. Suddenly he screamed. Moving his back against the mud bricks, he had trapped a small horned viper resting in a cavity in the cell's wall. Quickly John seized a stick and guided it outside. But it was too late. The robber moaned and held his neck where the skin had been deeply punctured.

By evening he was delirious. For three days and nights John and Nicholas tended him with all of the care and love due to a sick brother. It was only on the fourth day that the crisis passed and it seemed that he would live. Much weakened he managed, on the eve of that day, to sit up and take some herbs and soup, though he was unable to stand.

In the days that followed they learned that he was as poor as they. A soldier, he had deserted his lord's army in

Damascus and travelled down to Egypt living by his wits and his knife. His name was Matthew. Little by little, he told his story to his hosts. Little by little, they shared with him the story of the carpenter of Nazareth, to whom their lives were given.

***

> Though I walk in the midst of trouble,
> thou dost preserve my life;
> thou dost stretch out thine hand
>     against the wrath of my enemies,
>     and thy right hand delivers me.
>
> (Psalm 138:7)

As they finished the psalms for the early morning, Matthew came to speak with them.

'Sirs, I have used you badly.

> I came with hate to impale you.
>     You came with love to claim me.
>
> I came with violence to seize you.
>     You came with peace to free me.
>
> I came with greed to rob you.
>     You came with faith to enrich me.
>
> I came with death to slay you.
>     You came with life to restore me.

Surely I sit in darkness while you abide in light. Open the first gate of the desert path that I may begin my journey.'

Nicholas and John sat down with him. And for the rest of that day told him many things which he was to remember all of the days of his life.

As they came to the time for evening prayers, Nicholas with laughter beneath his words, said:

'Do not let your resolution to live the desert life waver. Remember the story of the foolish brother from Scete.

One day he found that rats had gnawed a hole in his sleeping blanket. So he determined to keep a dog to chase them away. Now the dog drank so much of the daily milk begged from his neighbours, that he decided to buy a cow. But the cow ate so much straw that he had to cultivate the land close to his cell to provide for it. This cow had calves, so he needed to engage labourers to tend them, to work in his fields and to build barns for his produce. He became a wealthy farmer. One day a brother from the desert came to Scete and enquired about this brother. The labourers were puzzled. They said, "There is no-one here such as you describe. Your former companion travelled on or is dead."'

'And all because a blanket had a hole in it', smiled Matthew.

\*\*\*

But God said to him, 'Fool! This night your soul is required of you; and the things you have prepared, whose will they be?'

(Luke 12:20)

# 12
# Prayer

*Take this loaf.*
*It is my body, broken for the bare things of the earth.*
*Do this for my remembering.*

*Take this wine.*
*It is my blood, a stream for the dry things of the earth.*
*Do this for my remembering.*

'Will you talk with the young man?'

The sun was still low when an elderly monk spoke to
Abbot Nicholas after the Sabbath Synaxis. He pointed to
a new brother, saying:

'Bessarion of Alexandria sent him here to seek for you.'

Brother Paul stood some distance away, his head bowed.
He had arrived in these wastes but a few days before.
The old man led Nicholas and John with the new brother
to the shade of a tree in the courtyard of his cell. Before
withdrawing, he gave them figs and water with which to
break their fast.

With honesty in his voice Brother Paul, tall with copper
hair and sparkling, grey eyes told his story. Youngest son
of the High Priest of the Temple of Apollo in Alexandria,
from his earliest years he was taught the service of the
god. He mixed incense, prepared the lamps and acted as
his father's assistant at the times of sacrifice. Twice each
year, he and his father ate rare herbs and it was at these
times that the god spoke to him in the Temple.

As his tale was told, he grew restless and perturbed.

Despite the cool of the shade, beads of sweat ran down his face.

'Prostrate on the steps to the altar I suspended all breath and passed from the gateway of reason. Entering a dream, I met each time that darker reality which as an unformed beast, waited to mark me for itself. Yet

Each time I awoke before the loathsome thing
   embraced me.
Each year as I entered the dream, he drew closer.
Each time as I sped from him, he hissed after me:

"Till your twentieth natal day!"

In obedience on every occasion, I reported to my father what had occurred. He told me to take the abomination into a loving caress, for it was the true form of the god. Each time when I could not, he bade my brothers beat me.

On my nineteenth natal day in great fear I fled from the Temple and by chance met Abbot Bessarion, who cares for all the brothers in the great monastery of Alexandria. He gave me shelter and kept me in hiding until it was safe to leave the city. In sending me to the stillness of these wastes, he bade me to seek you and your faithful disciple.'

As he finished he fell to his knees and wept.

'Since coming to this desert, the Dark One visits me each night. Though I eat no herbs and fast, still he comes. Each time now as I flee, I feel the heat of his breath and sense his touch upon me.'

Finally he sobbed with terror.

'To-morrow is my twentieth natal day!'

Nicholas drew him from his knees, embraced him and then sat with him holding both of his hands.

John slipped quietly into the guest cell and said the prayers and psalms for that time for them all.

***

> Jesus... rebuked the unclean spirit, saying to it, '... I command you, come out of him.' ... His disciples asked him privately, 'Why could we not cast it out?' And he said to them, 'This kind cannot be driven out by anything but prayer.'
>
> (Mark 9:25.28.29)

'Holy Father, how should I pray?'

The Abbot and Brother Paul had talked throughout the day. For the Brother it was as if the sun was slowly rising to bring its warmth and light to his darkened spirit.

Nicholas waited for a time and then said: 'Pray with many voices.

> Hear a maiden's laughter as the wind chases leaves.
> Know her mirth – 'tis a poem her life has yet to say.
> Feel her joy – as dawn's new light promises
>     His Rising.
> Hear the chord – her music joins the world's
>     eternal song.
>
> Hear a maiden's weeping as her soldier leaves
>     for war.
> Know the trust she puts in his fellow's screening
>     shield.
> Feel the stinging sharpness as an arrow threads
>     his throat.
> Hear death's ancient anguish in a lover's
>     mourning song.

Match your prayers to the myriad cries of His creation. Then set the Lord Christ within. Speak with His voice. Say:[11]

62

Abba, Father,
Abiding in each star and every childlike heart,
Sweet be your Naming.

Visit us with mercy and truth.
May all things in earth and heaven
Bend to the rule of your Love.

Our bread supply, though we be rich or poor.

Our sin forgive, deny its ancient clasp,
As we release him, whose wrongs are fixed
upon our heart.

From trials free us.
Break Satan's yoke from us.

Sovereign Lord,
Whose authority stirs the oceans,
Whose shining inhabits all that is,
Dwell with us. Amen.'

The darkness of night came quickly. It was decided that
Nicholas and John should remain with Brother Paul in
his cell. As an exile returning to his home country, the
young man was given a sweet sleep. Through the night,
as he entered his twentieth natal day, John and Nicholas
kept a vigil of prayer for him. At each hour, they said the
psalms quietly together.

Because you have made the Lord your refuge,
the Most High your habitation,
no evil shall befall you,
no scourge come near your tent.

(Psalm 91:9,10)

Before dawn, John went out to pick a posy of desert
grasses and wild flowers for Brother Paul's natal day.

# 13

# Hell

*... how are you to escape being sentenced to hell?*
(Matthew 23:33)

As John turned, he noticed that the small cloud of dust was much closer. A rider was travelling quickly through the wastes.

He filled his skin with water from the spring in the oasis, finished his cheese and dates and prepared to leave. Alexandria was now but half a day's walk away. Soon he would be able to rest at the house of Pinufius and speak with Sarah his wife. The Abbot remained in Nitria, his illness had left him too weak to journey. So the task, which could wait no longer, fell to the Dwarf.

The camel had been driven long and hard. It was clear that it could go no further without rest and refreshment. After nodding a greeting, the young man tended his strong beast with care and then sat to eat and drink. John, scooping water for him, noticed the richness of his clothes, the jewelled clasp that held his fur cloak and his fine leather sandals.

The traveller brushed aside a dusty tangle of yellow hair, and looked at John with shining in his eyes. Son of a wealthy, Christian merchant of Alexandria, his name was Philip. With mouth quick to smile and joy all brimming over, he said:

'I seek with speed to reach my house in our great city. there this day a maiden will give birth to her first child.'

Yet while he spoke John noticed riders coming with haste towards the oasis from Alexandria. As they approached, it was obvious that Philip knew them. Servants from his father's house, they had come to meet him. Unknowing, he rushed gladly to them.

He listened.

> Strange frosts
>     drew the cherry harvest to the ground.
> Sea's cold fingers scored out love's message on
>     the sands.
> He entered a windowless lodge for silence,
>     wherein dwell all who have no hope.
>
> Three bodies stayed for him.
> Out of time, they awaited burial in time.

His twin daughters were still born. The women had been unable to staunch his wife's haemorrhage.

While Philip and the servants spoke quietly with each other, the Dwarf withdrew to say his psalms and prayers.

> My heart is in anguish within me,
>     the terrors of death have fallen upon me.
> Fear and trembling come upon me,
>     and horror overwhelms me.
>
>                         (Psalm 55:4.5)

***

Before leaving with the servants, Philip walked slowly over to John and whispered with broken words:

'Sir, I see that you are one whose life treads the desert path to salvation. Teach me what I need to know in my distress. The sadness of these deaths is doubled for me. My wife and daughters are unbaptised. Do they now and ever inhabit a place of darkness?'

He wept as he sobbed these last words. John gently held his hand and said, with a deep stillness in his voice:

'Will He who fashions white violets, all grasses
  and their pods;
Should He who swells the barley and gives olives
  their highest berries;
Can He who counts the stars for joy and filters
  sandy crystal on shores unknown,
    Not love His own children?'

But John had not yet reached the heart of Philip's anguish. The young man said hesitantly:

'Each day goodness was resurrected in
  Rachel's spirit.
She gave alms to cripples, who begged at the
  city gates.
She bathed weeping sores of crones, whose
  flesh decayed.
She brought raiment for all who stood in rags
  and she put food in outstretched arms.

A sun for my life, she did not walk in faith,
  but followed the ancient gods.
Does she now and ever inhabit a place of darkness?'

John answered him with deep seriousness:

'Each day she gave coin to her Lord as He begged,
Anointed and bandaged His wounds as He cried,
Clothed a shivering nakedness as He wept, and
Fed a broken body as He sued for bread.
Will His Father not reward her for this mercy?'

But Philip pressed him further:

'Each month she lit a lamp for the old gods, burned
incense and lay in prostrate devotion before them.
Does she now and ever inhabit a place of darkness?'

John took time to answer, then said:

> 'When the great eagle, who can soar to Lebanon's highest peaks with grace, watches the unpolished fluttering of her young, will she be angered?
>
> When a little boy seeks to paint a likeness of his mother, will she show her rage at his tangle of coloured lines?
>
> Nor will God bring His wrath on those who walk honestly with the Word He has set secretly within their hearts.
>
> In His mercy, here and beyond, He ever leads His children. At different times, by many strange tracks, He brings us to the endless depths of an Infinity of Love, which is His Very Being.
>
> Remember this, Hell is love's extinction.
>   It grows in those who do not do justly,
>   will not reconcile the separated,
>   cannot show compassion for the needy.
>
> Remember this, Heaven is love's flowering.
> May your life continue her love – which is
>   His Love.'

As Philip and his servants wound their sad way towards Alexandria, John remained to pray. He remembered all whose lives were dry with growing sadness. He prayed that they might seek to walk again in the fresh waters of hope.

# 66

# Immanuel

*Who is this that comes from Edom,*
*in crimsoned garments from Bozrah...?*
*'Behold, your salvation comes...*
*and you shall be called Sought out'.*

(Isaiah 63:1; 62:12)

Lamps died and the house stood in purple darkness. The final part of John's journey to Alexandria had been un-eventful. Sarah and Pinufius, in deeply given love, were overjoyed to see him again. Little Ichabod, now nearly four, had claimed the Dwarf as his own special camel and ridden on his back most of the afternoon. In the evening he snuggled closely to his new friend. They both stared into the dying fire and John told him strange stories of the way to the land where children's shadows are made.

After the prayers and psalms for the late night were said, John lay quietly on his pallet and held this new family in his thoughts. He understood why young Pinufius had not told neighbours of his service as a monk in the monas-tery at Cellia. And why Sarah had not revealed that it was as she carried fresh vegetables to the monastery, that they had loved and conceived Ichabod. Certainly no more than half-a-dozen people knew that her father Arminion in drunken craze, had raped her while she secretly carried her child, and that in great anger at the loss of her virginity, her love for another and his own guilt, had beaten and cast her away from his household. And only the Abbot and he knew of Arminion's later attempted suicide and the mission to seek Sarah's for-giveness which her father had entrusted to the Dwarf.

Yet in all this dark web, it was to the child that John's thoughts were given. In him the world had once more been offered fresh hope. He knew that

There was set in the soul of Ichabod a music which would

> Sing for him in a darting smile as the sun feigned
>     'Hide' among portly clouds,
> Call to him as a laughing stream rushed boats of
>     jasmine leaf and willow to the brown sea,
> Beckon as his drummer-boy called clay soldiers to
>     battle with a horned desert lizard.

There was set in the soul of Ichabod a longing:

> To draw him to that seeking, without time or place,
>     Which begins at every hearth, at any hour.
> Yoked thus to the ancient gaze of priests from
>     Babylon,
> Fierce shamans of the North and strange Persian
>     magi,
> His end would be that beginning, where he
>     understood that
> The Holy One was within, lodging as a guest
>     beneath a tent.

There was set in the soul of Ichabod a mercy which would bring him

> To hold in love the brokenness of age;
> To be sentinel for those in suffering chains;
> To touch the tears of all who mourn for truth.
> To tend victims whose thoughts a tyrant ties;
> To bind blinded beauty's eyes
> And offer salve to slaves.

\*\*\*

For while all things were in quiet silence,
and the night was in the midst of her course,
thy almighty Word leaped down from heaven from
    thy royal throne.

(Wisdom 18:14-15)

Sleep would not come. John's thoughts moved from
Ichabod to the Christ who gave him being and light. He
was in awe as he pondered the end that was in His bud.

For

God's same messenger gave clue of His beginning
    to shepherds wrapped in furs and to th' aston-
    ished women at His end.[12]
Bound with bands, He was softly set on rock's cleft
    in secret cave at birth – and death.[13]
With burning eyes, in Salem's Temple[14] He con-
    founded twice those who sat on wisdom's bench
    – as Man and Child.[15]
This Babe in straw was hunted for dying by a
    king's decree – this Man was pinned in dying by
    Caesar's command.[16]
The ascending Son, sprung from death, spoke that
    blessing on Bethany's green – which ancient
    Zachary could not say.[17]

Did the Coming hold the Going?

He was in awe as he pondered the tree from which this
beauteous Rose came.[18]

For

Did not Tamar the Canaanite, for justice, veil her
    face and play the harlot by the road that leads to
    Timnah?[19]
Was not Rahab, who hid Joshua's spies on her roof
    among the flax, the harlot of Jericho?[20]

Was not Ruth, who came to glean in Bethlehem at
the barley harvest, from the land of Moab?[21]
Did not Bathsheba's beauty serve to draw Jerusalem's jealous king to murder and adultery?[22]
Was not God pleased to lodge His Glory in flesh
and overshadow a maid before she knew a man?[23]

Wisdom lost nothing.

He was in rapture as he pondered the threefold coming
of his Christ.

For

At the first, Eternal Word was cloaked in silence of
our flesh, enduring shame, despite and pain.
At the third, Eternal Word will vest in reckless love
and shepherd all time's dark creatures to dazzling glory.
In the second now He whispers secretly for those
whose hearts will turn about and say 'Come' to a
Beyond which is within.

In adoration silence brims over.

\*\*\*

The Dwarf completed his meditation by reading from
the gospel written by the holy John.

And the Word became flesh and dwelt among us,
full of grace and truth.

(John 1:14)

In the morning he decided that he would take a flask and
a loaf and go with Ichabod to the edge of the wilderness,
to see if a desert wind spoke his name.

# 15
# Sin

*Woe to those who call evil good and good evil...*
*who put bitter for sweet and sweet for bitter!...*
*as dry grass sinks down in the flame,*
*so...will..their blossom go up like dust.*

(Isaiah 5:24)

The grisly news arrived in the second week of John's stay in Alexandria with Sarah, Pinufius and little Ichabod.

The Dwarf had spoken to Sarah on behalf of Arminion her father.

'He pleads with you in these words,
    "Surely the bitterness of death is past."[24]
He says to me, "Take this for my daughter,
    a piece of money and a ring of gold." '[25]

At this her soul was stilled, though her young face remained deeply lined. After private thought, she asked that the coins be given to those in the city who protected orphaned children and that the ring be sold to care for poor widows.

Then she had said to John:

'Say to my father,"In winter when ice numbs the fields, seeds will not grow. Wait for spring. After five years direct my eldest brother to come to me. Perhaps then he may learn of forgiveness for you." '

It was Brother Paul whom Abbot Nicholas had sent with the news. Brought up in Alexandria, he knew it well.

Full of strength, he had travelled swiftly. His message he gave quietly and simply.

Arminion, Sarah's father, was dead. He had told her three brothers of the incestuous rape he had committed on their sister. He recounted how in his guilt, he had forced her from their home. He had hoped for pardon from them – as from Sarah. Yet they, inflamed with passionate anger, conspired together. Then they took him with force, though he did not resist, and hurled him down a well. So his neck was broken. This had all occurred a month ago.

> For everything there is a season...
> a time to weep, and a time to laugh;
> a time to mourn and a time to dance...
> a time to love and a time to hate.
>
> (Ecclesiastes 3:4)

As John and Paul were about to conclude the Scripture reading, the Dwarf prayed

> that the cool breeze of forgiveness would fan
>     Arminion's soul,
> that the wind of the Spirit would console
>     Sarah's heart and
> the breath of God bring understanding to the
>     three brothers.

They had both remained a further week to comfort the little family before leaving for the Nitrian wastes. Now about half a day's journey from Alexandria Paul said:

'Did the brothers do justly to take vengeance on the one whose incestuous rape violated their sister?'

'What is your judgement?' asked John.

73

'They acted justly,' he said. 'My judgement grows from this story:

'Once there was a prince who was heir to his father's throne. His half-sister was a princess, both wise and lovely. She was a virgin. Such was her beauty that his spirit was in torment, for he wished to take her but he could not. Then his friend, who was very cunning, devised a plan. "Feign illness upon your bed", he said, "and say to your father the king, Send my sister to my house that she might bake bread for me and I might eat from her hand."

He did all of this. Then the king sent to his daughter and said,"Go and prepare food for the prince." This she did. Quickly he dismissed the servants and said to his sister, "Bring the cakes to the bedroom that I may eat from your hand." She came. Then he took hold of her and said, "Be with me." Not wishing for this, she protested and drew back.

> But he would not listen to her; and being
> stronger than she, he forced her, and lay with
> her.
>
> (2 Samuel 13:14).

When it was done his passions changed and he hated his half-sister. His servant put her out of the house and bolted the door behind her. With torn garments and ashes on her head, she met her own brother. Understanding what had happened, he took her into his house. He counselled quietness and patience, though there was hatred in his heart.

After two years this brother arranged a great feast at the time of sheep shearing. He invited his half-brother and gave this instruction to his servants, "When the prince is merry with the wine, I shall command you to strike him dead." This they did and he who had committed incest and rape was killed.'

'And such was the way,' said the Dwarf, who knew the scripture 'that King David's son Absalom, took revenge on his half brother Amnon for the violation of the lovely Tamar.'[26]

'Justly took vengeance', he said, reminding John of his query.

They walked some distance. Then John spoke:

'Perhaps

There is a deeper wisdom than vengeance
    whose name is justice;
There is a deeper wisdom than justice
    whose name is mercy;
There is a deeper wisdom than mercy
    whose name is forgiveness;
There is a deeper wisdom than forgiveness.
    His name is Love.

A peach stone is knarred and strong,
Not to be crushed in a man's fist,
Or broken with his teeth.
Yet the gentle touch of soil and
The soft warmth of the sun,
Prompt its life.
    Love kindles morality.

Amnon was wanting in love: Absalom was wanting in love. Arminion was wanting in love: his sons were wanting in love. And so are we wanting in love.'

They continued the next few miles of their journey together in stillness of spirit.

# 16

# Clown

*Do not be conformed to this world but be transformed...*

(Romans 12:2)

'Sausages! On Good Friday!' With mock horror Brother Paul looked to the sky in disbelief while the Dwarf shook with laughter.

John's account of the eccentricities of the holy Justin had enlivened that afternoon's travelling. Returning from Alexandria and now but a day's journey from Nitria, they approached a ravine with many limestone caves where this strange, aged hermit dwelt. In need of refreshment and shelter for the night they called out to him.

A wizened little man, he came immediately to meet them and graciously led them to his cave. After washing and kissing their feet, he drew fresh water from the cistern for them and offered bread with figs and cheese. He knew Abbot Nicholas and listened intently as John told him of his master's sickness. They then said their psalms, prayed and read the Sacred Word.

> I am the Lord... who turns wise men back,
> and makes their knowledge foolish.
>
> (Isaiah 44:25)

After this, as was the tradition, the two brothers asked Justin to teach them. Quickly he said with a wide grin:

'And what could I tell you of wisdom, disciples of one who carries all wisdom? But I will tell you of foolishness.

There was a time when the Lord put it into my heart to travel to the north. So I journeyed for twenty days until I came to a city which was famous for the learning of its teacher. A proud man dressed in a fine tunic and a crimson woollen cloak, he taught under a canopy in the central square. Flattering disciples surrounded him.

"Ask what you will, and I will give answer", he challenged. So I said, "Once I heard some mysterious words which I hardly understood. Can you tell me their meaning? They are:

> Dniw fo htaerb elttil a tub si egdelwonk ym
> loof tnarongi na ma I taht won ees I." [27]

Immediately the teacher said:

> "I see now that I am an ignorant fool,
> my knowledge is but a little breath of wind."

At this all of his disciples rose and left him, feeling that they had been cheated. He had however construed the words correctly. Now a child who had stopped to listen laughed for he knew the game. He said to me:

> "Those disciples are too wise to learn foolish things.
> The shell of the almond is worthless but its kernel
> sweet, so they discard the fruit of the date and eat
> its stone."

Since that time I have taken as my only teachers the children who play at the gates of the town. Each month I go to them with dates from the desert. I ask that I might be allowed to eat the stones they spit out. In this way I remember the teaching of the Holy Apostle Paul whose words were:

> 'as for knowledge, it will pass away.'"[28]

He paused for a long while before saying: "There was another time when the Lord put it in my heart to go to the south. So I journeyed for forty days until I came to an important town. In it lived a greedy prophet with many hangers on. He spoke:

"Pay me one piece of gold and I will prophesy for you."

So I gave him gold and he told me of wars to come, famines and great disasters. Then I said to him:

"Let me prepare a feast for you. Tonight bring your friends to the inn by the great gate and we will all dine sumptuously."

When they arrived and were all seated I said to him:

"How can you know of the fall of kingdoms and the fate of princes and not know that I have no feast prepared for you and your friends!"

Now the inn-keeper had a small son who laughed at my joke and said:

> "These men are too wise to learn foolish things.
> If an idiot sits backwards on an ass they laugh,
> Yet perhaps it is the ass who walks in the
>     wrong direction!"

Since that time I have taken as the only prophets the children who play at the great gates of the town. Their imaginations are more true than false prophesy. Each month I visit them so that they may ride upon the back of this ass. In this way I remember the teaching of the Holy Apostle Paul whose words were,

> 'as for prophecies, they will pass away.'[29]

Again he paused for a long time before saying: "There was another time when the Lord put it in my heart to go to the east. So I journeyed for sixty days until I came to a famous city. In it was a priest of great renown. I had arrived on Holy Thursday. Seeing that beggars and the poor, prostitutes and thieves were not in church, I called to them saying:

"Come with me and you will receive great treasure."

Yet when we arrived at his church this priest would not receive us. He gave orders for the stewards to chase us away. On the next day, which was the day of the great fast, the Holy Friday of Our Blessed Lord's death, I returned to the church dressed in a fine linen toga and sandals of the softest calf skin. During this priest's homily I took from my satchel a sausage and began to eat it. Everyone was scandalised – save for a child who said to me:

"This congregation is too wise to learn foolish things. It is like a cat that complains because rabbits do not ask it to teach them to catch mice".

Since that time I have taken as my only priests, the children who play at the great gates of the town. Each month I visit them, taking for them cooked sausages. In this way I remember the teaching of the Holy Apostle Paul whose words were,

'make love your aim.'"[30]

"Three strangely wise children", mused Brother Paul as he and John left Justin the following morning. The Dwarf smiled.

"Perhaps they are children of his own heart."

Whoever humbles himself like this child, he is the greatest in the kingdom of heaven.

(Matthew 18:4)

# 17

# Mice

*I muse on what thy hands have wrought.*
*I stretch out my hands to thee: my soul thirsts for*
*thee like a parched land.*

(Ps 143:5-6)

Abbot Nicholas' cell was crowded, though only a desert mouse and he were within. His prayer filled its friendly space.

The Abbot's spirit was moved to glorify God.

He extolled his Creator

For sun and moon, ritual clocks for darkness and
  for light;
For earth's hued mantle, ox-eyed daisies and
  sprouting larch;
For folded mountains, piercing flints and
  uneasy, white seas.

He praised his Father

For bats and bees and moths, all things that flew;
For fish and eels, and dragons that dredged the
  ocean's paths;
For desert beetles and wandering mice and all
  earth's monsters.

He adored a Beauty Who, though ancient beyond record, was

A Father, springing fresh to create in the mists of
  green day;

A Son, embracing sharp sin's pain and still death —
  for a cure;
A Spirit, liberating all who sat in shadows —
  for joy and home.

The tiny mouse shuffled to the small table and began to nibble the crumbs which had fallen from it. Nicholas watched thoughtfully then:

His spirit was moved to give thanks to God.

He recalled his friends and generations unknown to him:

Marcellus of Corinth, all poets who caught the
  eternal chant;
Ann of Scete, all visionaries quivering to a voice
  yet unheard;
Paul of Antioch, all scholars, voyagers of the
  past and future.

He uttered blessings for

Children of the synagogue and all who dwelt in
  the old faith;
Pilgrims seeking Christ behind masks in painted
  jungle temples;
Those driven by doubt, who gazed at philosophy's
  silent stones.

He was mindful of

Kings who ruled their peoples with a single eye
  for justice;
Physicians whose art healed the body and trimmed
  the soul;
Friends whose love did not chain but opened being
  and becoming.

The mouse having feasted heartily then fetched a second, even smaller, who ate nervously while the other groomed himself.

'He brings his lady', laughed Nicholas...

... and his thoughts sped back sixty years to the Imperial Court in Rome. He had fallen in love with Messalina and she with him. Her intelligent, grey eyes and shy smile were burned into his soul. Their love had a passion and devotion which could only bud in two of seventeen years. But she was contracted to another, so her family quickly removed her to their estates in Sicily. He had no sight of her again. Later he heard that she had been given in marriage to an elderly tribune. Only the letter remained. She had sent it to him inside a book of poems by Catullus on the day she was taken from Rome. Though its ink on the kid had faded, fragments were etched on his heart.

'The gift of these poems is but the cense of my love. For the only gift of love is the giver...Your love created afresh for me the earth. With you I saw its blossom and bark as for the first time...

The pulse of love drives beyond what we can know. So a lover can never comprehend her beloved, for he is herald of a Beyond... He whom love seeks is Himself named Love...

Because her beloved cries tidings of Love Itself, he can never fulfil her.
    Thus love declares,"You are boundless",
    But knowledge says, "You have limits".
    All who love suffer this pain...

Do not two who truly love, seek to draw life each from the other? But what terror!
    Shall I poison you with the sickness of my
        being?
No, for in the love of two, there is a third.
    It is the Lord.
We draw life from One who proclaimed:

'He who eats my flesh and drinks my blood
    Abides in me, and I in him.'[31]

Nicholas watched as the two mice, having eaten well,
moved to the open door of his cell. They paused at its
shallow step and looked back at the Abbot. Then with
qu     ng whiskers and joyous squeaks, they tumbled
and scampered through his vegetable garden and across
the small courtyard into the vastness of the desert wastes.

Nicholas slapped his forehead. Once again his mind had
drifted! He had allowed two mice to break his meditation. Smiling wryly, he remembered how often this happened now. When this occurred his first master, Abbot
Julian the Good, used to teach him to pray briefly for
what was within the interruption and then conclude. So
Nicholas interceded for

    All who loved with a love that could not be
        returned;
    Those whose love was fractured by captivity,
        war and death;
    And those whose love was an enduring reproach.

John returned earlier than was expected. After the Abbot
had washed his feet and set cheese and water for him, the
Dwarf shared the news from Alexandria. Then he paused
and laughed.

'Approaching our gate, two mice together ran over my
foot, speeding from the garden. As I turned to watch they
stopped. Then the smaller went to the east and the larger
to the west'.

The Abbot looked to the north, to Sicily, and said
quietly:

            'Perhaps they were lovers.'

# 18

# Guiltless

*For, lo... fierce men band themselves against me...*
*for no fault of mine, they run and make ready...*
*Rouse thyself, come to my help...,*
*Lord God of hosts.*

(Psalm 59:3-5)

The sun hung like a huge orange on the horizon. One traveller had already sought shelter and retired for the night. Now John saw another with a mile yet to trudge before he could reach the hospitality of their cells.

The next morning the Abbot and his disciple arose early. They said their psalms and prayers and read from the Holy Gospels. Then the Dwarf took freshly drawn water to the two guest cells and invited each traveller to join the Abbot and him for breakfast.

The first to come to their table was Jacob. Swarth and wiry, he was a man grizzled by the years and now past the prime of his life. Yet his eyes were brightly alive and passionate. He spoke excellent Greek.

'My community is that of the Jews in Damascus. I practised as a physician in that city until the recent persecution of my people by the Emperor. Now I flee to cousins in Egypt.'

'You journey alone with only a flask and a staff?' queried Nicholas, curious that a person of distinction travelled as a common peasant.

Jacob laughed bitterly, 'Was not my race born to wander the earth in poverty without hope?'

'Surely God gives hope to all', exclaimed John. But he had spoken too quickly.

The silence was long and hurt. Then Jacob said seriously and very deliberately:

'My friend, the Roman garrison stands next to the great synagogue of Damascus. Three months ago, when soldiers arrested the city's most prominent Jews and took them to the garrison prison, their families and neighbours gathered at that synagogue on the Sabbath to pray for them. The rabbi read to us the portion appointed for the day:

> They came upon me in the day of my calamity;
> but the Lord was my stay. He reached from on high...
> he drew me out of many waters.
> He delivered me from my strong enemy.
>
> (Psalm 18:18.16.17)

While he read, we heard a fearful wailing as our friends were butchered with spears against the outer wall of the garrison.

Tell me, how could God remain in that synagogue and listen to our prayers, when through the wall His innocent sons were executed?

I fled from the synagogue to go to my home. But as I approached the street where my house stood, I saw it was in flames. Sarah, my wife, dearest companion for nearly fifty years, lay dead across our doorway. She, with her maidservant, had been hacked as soldiers entered the house. My neighbour Isaac sat in the gutter and wept his prayers:

> Help me, O Lord my God! Save me...
> Let my assailants be put to shame...
> The Lord... stands at the right hand of the needy,
> to save him from those who condemn him to death.
>
> (Ps 109 26.28.30.31)

Tell me, how could God remain in that street and listen to this prayer, when His innocent daughters lay dead before Him?

Hearing my young grand-daughter utter a piercing scream from within, I rushed through flames into my house and there I found her surrounded by a group of rough soldiers. I was seized and forced to witness her abuse and the murder of my whole family. As my father lay in the corner of the room, dying of his wounds, he whispered his final prayer:

> All day long foemen oppress me...
> for many fight against me proudly...
> they have waited for my life...
> This I know that God is for me...
> my enemies will be turned back in the day when
>     I call.

> (Psalm 56:1.2.6.9)

Tell me how could God remain in that room and listen to a prayer while carnage took place?

These men were about to kill me also when their centurion entered. He ordered them to take me to the great villa where Antoninus, the Proconsul and Governor, lived. His Chief Secretary and confidential Scribe, Lucullus, was sick and none of the physicians in the city had been able to cure him.

As I waited in an ante-room I stood by a screen and watched as Lucullus wrote a letter to the Governor's dictation. It was for the Proconsul in Antioch commanding him immediately to begin an extermination of that city's Jews. While waiting, my guard thinking I was too injured to move, left me for a brief time. Thus I was able to escape and quickly made my way from Damascus.

For this reason: I am in rough clothes having but flask and staff, I wander this wilderness without hope, I accuse God.

For this reason I wish to bring for trial:
    All who beat metal to fashion threading spears,
    Those who bake bread for legions and their slaves,
    All scribes whose letters bring the darkness of death,
    God for creating earth's most terrible monster –
        man.'

Nicholas and John were deeply moved. The Abbot said quietly:

'On what charge would you try the Holy One? Will you accuse Him for His gift of freedom to humankind?'

'For drawing so widely freedom's boundaries that appalling evil is born', was Jacob's reply.

    'If men may not choose wickedness:
        they have no freedom.
    If men are fenced from evil:
        they are without responsibility.
    Such men are neither good nor guiltless:
        for they are unfree'

 said the Abbot slowly.

At that moment the cell door opened and the second visitor arrived for breakfast. His complexion was ashen and his eyes deep set with pain. Plainly sick, John wondered how few months could be left of his life. He introduced himself.

'I am Lucullus, formerly Scribe and Chief Secretary to Antoninus, Proconsul and Governor of Damascus.'

# 19

# Fleas

*He rained flesh upon them like dust!*
(Psalm 78:27)

John watched as Nicholas moved over the sand in the first light of the morning, making the necessary preparations. On this, the Day of His Rising, it was the Abbot's turn to preside at the Eucharist for his brethren.

A broad stone was used for the altar. It seemed to the mind of the Dwarf to be crossed by the shadows of those men and women of every race who, from time's birth and with strange music, had sought to raise to the light the eyes of their companions.

All were assembled. Nicholas smiled with that sincere love which he had for all of his brothers. He greeted them warmly. Then slowly, he began:

'As the eyes of the watchman await the coming of
morning's light, so may our eyes seek Thee, O Lord,
in the dawning of this day.

Come to us in the unfolding of the earth.
Inhabit the stillness of our hearts.
Come to us in the breaking of the bread.
For truly Thou art our God.'

John's thoughts returned to the slave market in Corinth. He remembered how old Silvanus, deacon of the Church of Christ, had taken him, dying, from the filth of that place and nursed him to health again.

'Come to us...' He prayed that somewhere a stranger

stretched in sickness might be owned by his neighbour and each receive grace from the other.

Having called the brothers to awareness, Nicholas asked them to ponder the bitterness of sin and beg its removal from their lives.

'Holy Lord, we who darkly stumble in a far country for our sins, seek Thy pardon.

Bring us home that:

    Our iniquities against the Spirit,
    Our hardnes s towards friends,
    Our indulgence of ourselves,
    May be consumed in the welcoming embrace
        of Thy Love.'

John's thoughts returned to his childhood. He asked again to be forgiven the nightly blasphemies he had uttered as he lay, dirty and neglected, in the frightening blackness at the back of a hovel's shed where his bed was set. He had cursed God for

      the mis-shapen moulding of his body,
      the pain in his spine's unnatural arch,
      his daily mocking – as a parody of man.

'Bring us home...' He prayed for each crippled child whose spirit screamed in voiceless despair, that her anathemas might be absolved and her life lightened.

Nicholas first gave thanks over the cup.

'We thank Thee, Father, for the Holy Vine of David first brought out of Egypt and made known to us through Jesus, Thy Son: to Thee be glory for eternity.'

Then he gave thanks for the bread.

> 'As this broken bread, scattered on the mountains, was gathered together and made into one, so let Thy Church be gathered from the ends of the earth into Thy Kingdom: to Thee, Father, be glory for eternity.'

John's thoughts moved to the time that he and Nicholas had first met. Travelling through the wastes of Scete, the Abbot had asked for shelter in his cell. That night John was born anew. Nicholas had

> loosed a mind too tied by prayer,
> freed a spirit from destructive dogma,
> fed a body too full of fasting,
>     and let him laugh.

'Broken bread... gathered together...' he prayed for every slave denied the fruit of the earth; for those unable to share in the celebration of new life; and for himself, that deeper compassion might be his.

After they had all partaken of the bread and shared the cup, Nicholas said:

> 'We thank Thee, Father, for Thy Name, which Thou hast caused to dwell in our hearts and for the faith and immortality which Thou hast made known to us through Jesus. Be mindful of Thy Church to perfect it in Thy Love. Gather it from the four winds that, sanctified, it may take that place which Thou hast prepared for it.'

John's thoughts moved like broad splashes of coloured paint. Across his life he saw

> joy crossed with agony,
> security torn by suffering,
> love wounded in betrayal.

90

'To dwell in our hearts...' John prayed that there may be

to the east and the west, the north and the south,
those whom the Spirit had kissed,
    that they might unite
        what was passing with the All Surpassing,
        what was bounded with the Unbounded,
        what was dying with the Ever-Living.
    Thus would the fragments be taken into the Whole.

'May grace come and this world pass away', said Nicholas.

'Hosanna to the God of David', the brothers replied.

'Maranatha', he whispered, standing very still.[32]

'Amen', they returned.

John prayed finally that the Lord might come and
    turn the desert waste to grass and running waters,
    burn with fire the soldiers' trampling sandals and
    bring life to the barren and gladness to the desolate.


Having partaken of His Lord's incorruption, the Dwarf quietly watched the Abbot. The others gradually completed their prayers and withdrew. Once Nicholas started to move John quickly went to help him. He sat on a low rock and rubbed his bare foot vigorously. Laughing, he looked up.

'I think that during our Eucharist, a sand flea and her tiny family have feasted on my foot!'

# 20

# Fraction

*Search me, O God, and know my heart!*
*try me and know my thoughts!*
*... and lead me in the ancient way.*

(Psalm 139:23.24)

Lucius arrived, as he had promised, at the time of the autumn rains. Each second year he fulfilled his vow to journey from Rome for Nicholas' counsel. The Abbot had taught him to walk the 'Way' and though he had great estates banking the River Tiber, he lived simply. His wealth was distributed to orphans and widows, to those whose bodies were racked and minds crazed.

He took private counsel with the Abbot, giving him many letters from old friends and the churches in Rome. John prepared a meal, after which they sat together to talk in the shade of the lemon tree, outside the guest cells.

'What of the Church in Rome?' asked the Dwarf, eager for news.

Lucius paused and looked at Nicholas who said to him,

'Speak plainly, for we are trusted friends.'

'Sadly at present, there are factions', said Lucius seriously.

'The first faction is led by Thomas the Weaver.

In his Church

> The altar is a table of burnished gold,
> Priests' vestments are of embroidered silk,
> Exact worship continues by day and night.

Outside his Church

> The poor are clad only in tattered rags
> With the smoke of candles for comfort and
> The prayer of empty words for food'.

'The letters you bring speak of him', said Nicholas, pondering. 'He seeks to bind God with the crowd of his prayers. But if Jesus the Carpenter refused to constrain God – and turn stones to bread – why does Thomas the Weaver succumb to this temptation?[33]

Does he not understand that

> God is ever sought but never found,
> Ever new, thus never known.
> Not subject or object,
> He precedes both.'

At this point they broke off to say the psalms together.

> Unless the Lord builds the house,
> those who build it labour in vain.
> Unless the Lord watches over the city,
> the watchman stays awake in vain.
>
> (Psalm 127:1).

Then Lucius continued, 'The second faction is led by James the Potter.

In his Church

> He claims miracles for the faithful,
> Proclaims healings for the pure and
> Explains the ways of God to the wise.

Beyond his Church

The destitute labour in fields to feed the mighty,
The sick hide their pain in dark cells and
Slaves with no hope await the pit'.

'The letters you bring also speak of him,' said Nicholas slowly. 'He seeks the proof of Divinity in his own delusion. But if Jesus the Carpenter refused a sign – and would not step from the pinnacle of the Temple – why does James the Potter succumb to this temptation?[34]

Does he not understand that

> The Lord is as One who walks beneath the sea
> > and makes no tracks.
> He is patient with the wicked but tests the pure.
> He speaks to children but sets the clever in the
> > darkness of a maze?'

They left their discussion to read a portion from the Holy Gospels.

> An evil and adulterous generation seeks for a sign; but no sign shall be given to it except the sign of the prophet Jonah. For as Jonah was three days and three nights in the belly of the whale, so will the Son of man be three days and three nights in the heart of the earth.
>
> (Matthew 12:39-40)

Lucius continued, 'The third faction is led by John the Tanner.

In his Church the faithful

> Count their rewards,
> Separate themselves from sinners and
> Condemn the weak.

Without this Church stand those

> whose hearts are uncomprehending,
> whose minds are clouded and
> whose bodies are spent.

'He too, is spoken of in my letters', said Nicholas quietly. 'He is puffed out with pride. But if Jesus the Carpenter saw that the way to glory lies in poverty, wretchedness and obedience – for he refused to worship Satan – why does John the Tanner succumb to this temptation?[35]

Does he not understand that

> The one who is nothing has most,
> The one who is broken is taken up and
> The one who surrenders is conqueror?'

Once more they broke off to read the Song of Mary the Virgin.

> He has scattered the proud in the imagination of their hearts, he has put down the mighty from their thrones, and exalted those of low degree; he has filled the hungry with good things, and the rich he has sent empty away.
>
> (Luke 1:51-53)

For many months after the departure of Lucius, the Abbot and the Dwarf continued to pray for Thomas the Weaver, James the Potter and John the Tanner that they might be blessed by the Father, saved by the Son and inhabited by the Spirit, and know that the Way lies on a path of love which has three gates:

> the failure of understanding,
> the forgetfulness of self and
> the remembrance of others.

# 21

# Story

*But these words seemed to them an idle tale, and they did not believe them.*

(Luke 24:11)

'What is in your chest, brother?' boomed Abbot Matthias of Scete to Nicholas, with undisguised curiosity. John disliked it when Matthias stayed as a guest, which he now did twice each year. For he was an Abbot of strong views with whom it was easy to disagree.

'Why, my books', said Nicholas lightly – and rather too innocently. He raised the lid of the large box and carefully unpacked several small volumes.

'Some, like the Catullus, the Homer and the Plato, have been with me many years. Others, like the Pliny and the Cicero, have been given more recently.'

First Matthias frowned. Then he turned and with some anger, fiercely criticised Nicholas for receiving and reading books by pagan authors.

'Such works pollute the eyes, defile the mind and corrupt the spirit. They are a door for Satan to enter this cell. Have regard for your simple disciple, if not for yourself!'

John thought that Nicholas would have laughed had he not been disturbed by the passion with which Matthias spoke.

The Abbot drew him to a bench and they sat together. Then Nicholas said with just the hint of a mysterious smile:

'Many years ago in a village far from here, there lived a poor camel driver. His most valuable possession was a small lime tree. It gave no fruit. But once a year at night during the great fast, it would bear a single blossom. And in that blossom's heart was a beautiful and rare emerald.

Now each time the camel driver kept watch in his garden to collect this priceless jewel, he fell asleep. Always he awoke just as a tiny, red monkey plucked the blossom, seized the emerald and fled into the great desert which lay beyond the village.

After this had happened for the seventh time he decided to search for the monkey.

For many days he wandered in the wastes of the desert. It seemed to have no end. But he could not find the monkey. He was about to give up and return home, when he saw a dove on the branch of an almond tree. It told him to travel to the north for three days until he came to a great oasis. "There you will find the monkey asleep in a tree. On each side of the tree a cord is tied. Bind the monkey with that on the left. Ignore the other, else it will be the worse for you."

At the end of his journey, the camel driver found everything exactly as the dove had said. As he began to untie the cord on the left, he noticed that it was dirty, of poor quality and frayed. That on the right was new and woven with silk and gold thread. "It is surely more sensible to use the better cord," he said. So he took the one on the right. No sooner had he tied the monkey than robbers arrived at the oasis. They beat him, stole what he had and cast him naked into the desert. He knew that without water and cover, he must soon die. As he sat waiting for death, he wept bitterly.

It was then that he saw the dove again. She flew to him and said: "This has come about because you did not listen to me. However, foolish though you are, I feel sorry for you and will help you again. Go but an hour to the east and you will find two trees and a small pool. There refreshment, clothing and a strong spear await you. Take them and journey to the south. After forty days of travelling your path will divide. Continue on the left path, do not use the right else it will be the worse for you."

And after forty days the camel driver found everything as the dove had said. He stood before two paths. The one to the left looked desolate and was crowded with thorns. It led into a dark ravine where there were many rocks. The one to the right led into a sunny valley. There was green pasture and he could see people laughing, feasting and dancing. They were calling to him to join them. He felt very inclined to go to the right and debated carefully with himself about which path to take. Once he moved a little into the green field. Then he stopped and said: "No! Although the way of the dove looks forbidding, I will trust her and follow it."

It was a painful way. It had swamps and dangerous cliffs. Upon the way he had to fight a flying dragon and a great snake. Eventually, after many months' travel and adventures too numerous to tell, he was surprised to find that the path was familiar. Suddenly he turned a corner and recognised his own village. Entering his house, he found in a cage on the table the little red monkey. On a piece of silk next to it were seven, beautiful emeralds.'

At the end of the Abbot's story there was a very long silence. Matthias of Scete was not a fool. 'Shall I interpret?' he asked in a voice that seemed chastened. Nicholas nodded.

'Your story,

      makes outward those things that are inward,
        constructs each thought as an action.

  A believer must recast them into her soul's journey.

  The camel driver enters upon a quest for emeralds:
        The believer seeks for God.

  The camel driver leaves his livelihood for this quest:
        The believer gives up what she values.

  The camel driver does not heed the dove's first advice:
        The believer strays and falls into many temptations.

  The camel driver walks the difficult path with faith:
        The believer treads the 'Way' carrying a cross.

  The camel driver discovers that his treasure is at home:
        The believer finds that He has ever dwelt in her heart.

      Thus may God inhabit the tales of all story-tellers
        and poets.'

After this the brothers ate and prayed together, then Matthias departed for Scete.

'What wonders a little story from the pagan Severinus, will work for a Christian hermit', joked Nicholas.

'And for a simple disciple!' said John with mock pomposity.

Then they both roared with kindly laughter.

# 22
# Disciple

*The sons of Zadok, who kept the charge of*
*my sanctuary... shall teach my people*
*the difference between the holy and the common.*

(Ezekiel 44:1.23)

'He appears not to be coming to us, so let us go to him', said Nicholas, with a puzzled expression on his face. John looked, and the boy who was perhaps twelve or thirteen years old, still sat about half a mile away. He had been there, unmoving, for nearly an hour.

As they came to him, he tried to kneel and kiss their feet. But Nicholas quickly drew him up and asked if they could give him simple nourishment for his journey. He accepted and added as if under his breath: 'My journey is now finished.'

It was obvious to John that he had not travelled far that day. There was no more than the finest layer of sand dust on his richly lined cloak and his fine goatskin sandals were unstained. A sturdy young lad, growing well, he had black hair which curled carelessly around a tanned and serious face. His dark eyes were at once eloquent and inscrutable.

'My name is Peter of Ephesus. I seek to serve John the Dwarf and become a disciple of Abbot Nicholas the Wise, both of whom I have now found.'

Again he tried to kneel but John sat him back on the bench. Then they both listened carefully as he told them why he had come.

100

'I lived as a child in a villa whose gardens ran to the sea.
Often, when alone, my spirit was taut and in a glint I saw

Sea's water spark and grasses' blades ablaze
     with suns unveiled;
Swans sweet swimming and spiders' spired wheeling
     held newly seen.
This fire rested in each blossom, though yet beyond;
It came as a memory from the past, still to be.'

As he spoke Nicholas too remembered those moments in
his own life, when light pierced his spirit and song
bound his heart though neither wounded, rather healed

The cold red of dying sun behind winter's
     naked trees,
What were they waiting for?
New sprung rushes on quiet brook's banks
     hiding heron's egg.
Where had they come from?
Each moment made him feel an hundredfold;
     But why and how and for what?

When Peter had eaten the dates and cheese offered to
him and drunk the water, they moved outside to pray and
to read the Scriptures.

Lo, these are but the outskirts of his ways;
and how small a whisper do we hear of him!

(Job 26:14)

Then the lad continued speaking:

'How could I believe the unbelievable?
How could I speak of what dwelt in silence?
How could I know the inconceivable?

Only Anthony, deacon of the Church in Ephesus, was
able to guide me. He spoke these words to me:

101

"The failure of understanding is the very track
    to God.
  Knowledge is not stones, but a voyage;
  Wisdom is not words, but a childlike heart;
What stands at the forefront of the mind's stage,
    matters not a wrack.
Recall rather summer's recesses and life's
    secret place.
  In a niche the mustard seed will grow."

He taught me each Sabbath afternoon:

To see no life, dung beetle or scavenging rat,
  as trivial, meriting destruction;
To be astonished at earth which held greenery and
  deserts and river horses.
To perceive that explanations live but a short time
  and are refreshed again in mystery.
To understand that life's meaning is but partially
  seen for God continually bestows His grace and
  makes riddles.

When he could teach me no more he said: 'It is rumoured that, among the monks in the barren wastes of Nitria are two, an angel and an archangel. Send by God, they teach all who travel to them His ways." '

'No need for these when His Son has come', said Nicholas quickly.

There was a long silence which the Abbot and the Dwarf both allowed. Finally Peter spoke as to them both:

'For this I have come. Will you take me to be your servant and disciple that I may learn to walk the desert pathway?'

Nicholas looked gravely at him. And John realised that he was concerned about the lad and yet had sensed the finger of God upon him. He said:

'My answer is neither "No" nor "Yes". For it is not yet time to give an answer. My word is this:

Return home.
Submit yourself to your family. Honour your parents.
Love your friends and do good to your neighbours.
Return good for evil, forgive your enemies and
    fast weekly.
Worship with the brethren. Let them continue to
    teach you.
The first lesson of the desert life is obedience.
This we now place upon you.
If, after the passage of eight years, this thing is still
    in your heart, return to us and we will receive you
    with joy.'

And now comes his father, thought John, as he saw a comfortable man in his early forties, obviously a merchant of considerable means, heading anxiously towards their cells. His camel was ahead of the others. Servants, no doubt, John thought. He noticed, too, one camel without a rider.

It was indeed as John and Nicholas had guessed. Early that morning Peter had left his father's caravan, which lodged overnight at the nearby oasis. Since hearing of them from Anthony the deacon in Ephesus, the lad had determined to be their disciple. The route into Egypt which his father's caravan had taken, had given him the chance to meet them.

As they watched the caravan move away, now with young Peter – and a sore ear – Nicholas said to John, with a twinkle in his eye: 'And which of us, do you think, is the Archangel?' They laughed with delight and this remained a joke between them for the rest of that year.

# 23

# Maze-maker

*So now send me a man skilled to work in gold,*
*silver, bronze, and iron, and in purple, crimson,*
*and blue fabrics, trained also in engraving.*

(2 Chronicles 2:7)

The horse rose on its hind legs. Its head was thrown to the sky and its mane wildly flowing. It looked as if it would leap from the palm of Silas' hand. No taller than a finger, it was carved with delicacy and fine skill in rare white ivory.

'My father, Silas the Elder, sends his greetings and this gift to Nicholas, the friend of his youth. He says, "Though the time of our growing is gone, the memory of our friendship remains. Through all this long life it has been a lamp to bring light for my path." '

Silas the Younger was squat and strong. Though of mature years, there was but little grey in his dark beard. A cheerful man, he smiled easily, was self-assured and had the most penetrating blue eyes that Nicholas had ever seen. An architect and worker in metals, he was on his way to Pontus, commissioned by its Governor to build a labyrinth. Whilst in Alexandria, he had broken his journey to fulfil the dear wish of his father that Nicholas should receive a gift.

Before they ate, the readings and psalms were said.

Zillah bore Tubal-cain; he was the forger
of all instruments of bronze and iron.

(Genesis 4:22)

Afterwards John asked their guest about his creative work. Nicholas listened quietly, though it seemed as if part of his mind was elsewhere. Silas said:

"My work has five parts.

> The first is a search in the world. Creators
>> Seek patterns in a peacock's fan or petals' posy,
>>> in riding moon or dancing stars;
>> Seek values in lovers' tears or brother's blood,
>>> in king's decrees or judge's rule;
> For these construct intent and purpose, bringing
> meaning.
>
> The second is an awareness of the world. Creators
>> Rub sleep from their eyes and gaze at the shining,
>> Explore prodigality overspilling its moulds;
> We embrace all that is, in our journey to new lands.
>
> The third is an intimacy with all that surrounds.
>> Creators
>> Conjoin what is beyond and within, what is above
>> and beneath;
>> Tie with invisible threads what has life and what
>> has dryness;
> We commingle contraries.
>
> The fourth is to bring to blossom what is in bud.
>> Creators
>> Fix no limits but allow to be,
>> Ride all horizons to reach the sun,
>> Begin a pilgrimage on earth which is only
>> fulfilled in heaven.
>
> The fifth is a growth into the source of mystery.
>> Creators
>> Remove old gates and walk in fresh meadows,
>> Fit no theorems and inhabit paradoxes.
>>> The end is this: We create Love."

John thought about this for a while and then said:

'Friend, I have a question. Is not the whole of this an ascent to God? For

Is it not God who prompts the artist's search?
Is it not His mark on all creation of which there
   is awareness?
Is God not girt round with the marriage of
   contraries?
Is He not ever creating anew and bringing to fruit?
Is He not Himself that Mystery whose name is
   Love?'

'True – perhaps', smiled Silas.

Then with a robust grin he went on:

'My father says that each person is born with her back to God. Only an artist or poet may turn her around.'

While Silas spoke Nicholas had recalled his friendship with his father, Silas the Lame. More than six decades had passed since they were boys together, tutored by Democritus at the Imperial Court in Rome. Both were sons of powerful tribunes. Nicholas remembered vividly those exciting afternoons when the Captain of the Emperor's Cavalry came to teach. But he would not allow Silas to have a horse. When Nicholas sought to persuade him, he earned a cuff and an explanation: 'His twisted legs have no strength.'

It was then that he and Silas conspired with each other. Daily and in secret, before the sun's rising, they rode together on his own horse. One morning as the two were seated on noble Tarquinius, a young horse with spirits as high as his masters', Nicholas slid down to let Silas ride alone for the first time. He watched as Tarquinius, knowing, flew. It was then that the crippled boy was born anew. As the wind blew to his face, God breathed upon him.

Despite the years, Nicholas could recall the passion and the joy which burned in Silas' sparkling blue eyes as he drew heaving Tarquinius to a halt before him. Forever now, Silas' life would be different.

'I too, have a question', said Nicholas quietly. 'From whence does your art arise?'

'Inspiration has five parts', said Silas, after some thought.

'Each artist wrestles with wood or marble; with clay or colour, and in that wrestling is thrown. Such defeat is a pain which rests deeply in the heart and may stay. Yet suddenly the pain is healed. The image which unifies, for which the wrestling occurred, is given. Next this image shapes pattern or poem, song or weaving. Finally it is received and interpreted by those who hear or look, touch or taste.'

'And is it not God who draws the healing image in the spirit? And is this artist's creation not the fulfilment of God's secret will?', asked Nicholas.

'True – perhaps', smiled Silas again.

The Abbot and the Dwarf turned towards the cells again, having watched Silas disappear into the sands. Nicholas was still holding the tiny prancing horse. He passed it to John and said: 'My eyes are weary. What tiny writing is beneath it?'

'Just one word', said John, 'Tarquinius.' Nicholas smiled.

Then they prayed for all who created, that they might feel the breath of God upon them, and disturb men and women with the beauty and truth of their work.

# 24

# Slave

*O Lord God of hosts, how long wilt thou be angry*
*with thy people's prayers? Thou hast fed them*
*with the bread of tears.*

(Psalm 80:4.5)

The baby cried lustily. And the young woman realised at once that she had interrupted Nicholas and John and the Lady Helena in their prayers. She stood nervously by the open door, carefully carrying her little daughter. Nicholas looked at the other two and said quickly:

'The Lord is in no mood for our worship this morning. He bids us show hospitality and be doing.'

As they had guessed, Anna was yet another runaway slave heading for Alexandria, trying to save her baby from death at the hands of her master. John set a meal, filled her satchel and waterskin, while Nicholas gave her a route for that city which would allow her to rest with other brothers and take refreshment in the oases. The Lady Helena, who regularly stayed with the Abbot prior to the Feast of the Holy Child, played gently with the tiny baby.

Anna would not remain for more than the three hours it took to regain her strength and attend to the needs of her daughter and herself. She feared pursuit. After they had watched her disappear into the safe arms of the ever-changing sands, they returned to the courtyard. The Abbot and the Dwarf could see how moved the Lady Helena was by the incident.

It was during the evening as they talked together that she said:

"Suppose that an old and rich chieftain had a wife and that his wife was unable to bear him children. Suppose also that the wife had a young slave from another land and that she said to her husband:

"Take my slave. Be with her. Thus I may have my child."

And he went to her and she conceived. But the wife came again to her husband and said:

"My slave holds me in contempt because she has conceived when I could not."

But her husband reminded her that, this slave was in her power and she could do with her whatever she wished. Then the wife dealt harshly with the slave and so afflicted her, that in the end she ran away.

While she was by a spring of water in the desert, an angel spoke to her in her troubles and promised that she should have many descendants from her unborn child. He also declared that the baby's name would be "God Hears".[36] Though he warned that as he grew, he would be at odds with his own people and in strife against them. Then the angel commanded this slave to return to her mistress and submit herself to her. This she did and gave birth to her son.

God then bestowed his grace and this chieftain's wife conceived. As her child grew he played with the son of the slave. The wife was disturbed, for she realised that the presence of the slave's child threatened the inheritance for her own son. She went to her husband and said:

"Send my slave and her child away."

Now he was unwilling to do this. But the voice of God spoke to him telling him to do as his wife wished, for this younger son would be the father of nations. So very early one morning, he gave the slave a skin of water and a loaf of bread, and cast her out with her child into the desert.

Finally, when all food and drink were gone and it seemed as if they must die, the slave laid her child beneath a bush and went to sit some distance away to weep. She could not bear to watch him perish. Then God spoke to her and told her to pick up her son. He showed her a well with water in it. She gave the child a drink and they both survived. They lived in the wilderness of Paran and God protected the son. He grew to be a fine bowman and eventually

> his mother took a wife for him
> from the land of Egypt.
>
> (Genesis 21: 21)

Now suppose all these things and then tell me this: How is such a story to be understood?"

They thought awhile and it was John who answered first.

'In the story what is common becomes particular. For there is enmity between women who are barren and those who are fertile. So Rachel envied Leah.[37] So Peninnah provoked Hannah.[38] In your story Hagar the slave has contempt for Sarah her mistress. Later she fears that Ishmael will take the inheritance from her own son Isaac and appeals to Abraham to send her away.'[39]

Then Nicholas spoke:

'Hagar is a servant who suffers in innocence.
She foreshadows
> Those whom men abuse for secret purposes;
> All enslaved without hope of justice;
> Those drawn to conflict without their consent.

Hagar is an Egyptian slave in a Hebrew family.

She foreshadows
> Those alien and fearful in a strange land;
> All wandering in places far from home;
> Those with families who flee for their lives.

Hagar is a woman lost beneath oppression.

She foreshadows
> Those whom the powerful use;
> All cast-out to starve;
> Those who watch as their children die.'

Then the Lady Helena spoke quietly:

'Let us pray for women in whose lives
> There is an exodus without promise;
> There is a revelation without hope;
> There is exile without return.

Let us pray for children
> Whose lives are cast in the shadows;
> Whose spirits are crushed with fear;
> Whose bodies are tormented by pain.'

And Nicholas concluded:

'Let us remember also those who believe that the Lord
God has:
> Rejected their prayers,
> Set aside their cause and
> Ordained their desolation;
that beyond Gethsemane's dark trial and Calvary's
nightmare may lie for them, the new light of resur-
rection's dawn.'

# 25
# Cave

*A Maskil of David, when he was in the cave.*[40]
*Bring me out of prison that I may give thanks to thy name!*
*The righteous will surround me;*
*for thou wilt deal bountifully with me.*

(Psalm 142:7)

'Soon it will be time for me to go', said the Abbot thoughtfully as he sat peeling onions and watching John weed the vegetable garden. The sun had risen but an hour and its heat was not yet fierce, so John stopped his work and came to sit with his dear friend and master on the bench beneath the lime tree.

They sat together in that silence which deeply binds all of those who pursue birth. Then the Abbot said:

'When I was a boy in Rome I lived in a villa set in beautiful gardens and a fine park. Beyond were woods where my father hunted with his friends. One day I followed them into the woods but could not run quickly enough to catch them. About to return home I caught sight of a cave in the side of a steep rise. Strangely I had not seen it before. At its entrance a small child beckoned to me. I walked to her and, without speaking, she took me by my hand and drew me to the back of the cave. As we walked down a long passage I heard still music of great beauty which prompted the thought:

Always you are a beginning.

Then we entered into a dazzling loveliness of colours and scents, of shapes and sounds such that my tongue could not utter. It was a poem more perfect than I had hitherto known. I was intoxicated, for

> It was as joyous as a great marriage feast;
> It was as companionable as breaking bread
> with friends;
> It was as happy as picking first grapes from
> the vineyard.

Then suddenly a darkness came and I was being shaken. My father had found me lying on the ground. "You stumbled and struck your head against this tree", he said.

I cried, though not for my soreness, but for the paradise which had gone.

When I was a young man at the Imperial Court in Rome twice more I saw the cave. The first was when the Emperor had summoned me to a private audience. I knew that he was going to offer me my dearest wish, the charge of a legion. Delayed by crowds on their way to the Circus I was late. I left my horse with a soldier and sped through the palace gardens as quickly as I was able. In a grotto I saw again the cave and the little maiden beckoning. I paused and heard the faint sound of a wordless song. It prompted the thought:

> All your skill is not a beginning.

But I dared not stay and sadly rushed past the child to the Emperor's chamber. I was given the charge of a legion. Yet before I could take it up, my father was called to be Governor of Pisidia and I was required to remain in Rome to manage the family estates.

The second was when my mother had died. Many attended the rites, for daily she gave bread to the poor and anointed with ointment the sores of those who came to our gates. Her wealth meant little to her. The priests had almost concluded the rites and I was about to rise and deliver the encomium when the cave appeared before me. At its entrance was the same child. I stayed long enough to listen to the pan pipes as they played their haunting music. The pipes prompted the thought:

The beginning was yesterday and will be tomorrow.

I ignored my vision and did a son's duty. I did not know whether the sadness which overwhelmed my heart was due to my mother's death or my refusal to go with the child.

After this, through decades of years, I did not see the child again. That is until last evening. Do you remember, I was sitting in the courtyard weaving a basket while you were digging? The mouth of the cave appeared in the wall of the cell and the little one beckoned more urgently than before. A six-stringed instrument touched my soul with its singing. It prompted the thought:

Soon the beginning will be lost.

I was about to take the little girl's hand when, at our gates, the snorting of camels and the noise of merchants needing water for themselves and their beasts, persuaded me to stay. Through the night I watched the darkness of the desert and sky and know now that I must leave Nitria and all my brothers here. I have to walk the path to a deeper quiet in a hidden place. Soon I shall leave. Will you journey with me, friend of my soul?' Before John answered, they said their psalms together.

...he shall hide me in his pavilion...
he will conceal me under the cover of his tent.[41]
(Psalm 27:5)

Like cold water to a thirsty soul
so is good news from a far country.
(Proverbs 25:25)

114

After this John knelt before his master and said:

'How will the turtle dove live without her mate?
How may the carp swim without a pool?
How will the grass be green without the dew?
    Neither can I be without you.

Will there be bud and blossom without the sun?
Will hawk's eggs hatch without a mother's warmth?
Will a lover delight in life without a beloved true?
    Neither can I be without you.

Though you reject me, yet I will follow you;
If you look to lose me, I will seek to find you;
When you cast me out, I will lie at your door;
    For I cannot be without you.'

Then each embraced the other from that spiritual love which only those who truly follow Christ can show.

So it was that letters were written to Rome, to Alexandria, to Corinth and all places where the Abbot's disciples dwelt. These, with books and some clothes, were left with the brethren.

Thus Nicholas and John were driven once more into the desert. They headed for the great silences which dwelt over the vast wastes of Scete. None watched as they slowly began to walk the Way set for them. The hot wind blew sand over the vegetable garden and swung the door of the cell backwards and forwards, backwards and forwards...

Always you are a beginning.

# Notes

1. The Nitrian desert lies about 40 miles south of Alexandria and 50 miles west of Cairo. It takes its name from the *natron* (soda) which was collected there.

2. Scete lies 40 miles south of Nitria.

3. The narrative of the sacrifice of Jephthah's daughter occurs in Judges 11.

4. Exodus 14:23-30.

5. Judges 16:23-30.

6. Phenice is Phoenicia.

7. The Synaxis was a meeting which could be for prayer or the celebration of the Eucharist.

8. Pispir is 60 miles to the south-east of Nitria.

9. Spikenard is a precious ointment. Jesus was anointed with it by a woman as he sat in the house of Simon the leper (Mark 14:3).

10. Revelation 22:2.

11. Matthew 6:9-13.

12. Luke 2:10-12 and 24:5-6.

13. Luke 2:7 and 23:53. (The manger may have been a cave and the fodder for the beasts set upon a rock or shelf in it).

14. Salem is another name for Jerusalem.

15. Luke 2:47 and 20:26.

16. Matthew 2:16 and Luke 23:24.

17. Luke 24:50 and 1:21-23.

18. The genealogy of Jesus in Matthew's gospel (1:1-16) mentions five women through whom the line to the Messiah came. They had unusual backgrounds or scandalous relationships with their partners.

19. Genesis 38.

20. Joshua 2.

21. Ruth 1:4.

22. 2 Samuel 11.

23. Matthew 1:18.

24. 1 Sam 15:32.

25. Job 42.11.

26. The story of Amnon's abuse of Tamar occurs in 2 Samuel 13.

27. To read these two lines correctly read from right to left and begin with the second line.

28. 1 Corinthians 13:8.

29. 1 Corinthians 13:8.

30. 1 Corinthians 14:1.

31. John 6:56.

32. *Maranatha* is the Greek form of an Aramaic expresion often translated as 'Our Lord cometh' (1 Corinthians 16:22). This and some other expressions in Nicholas' prayers reflect a second century A.D. account of the Eucharist in a document called the *Didache*.

33. Luke 4:3-4.

34. Luke 4:9-12.

35. Luke 4:5-8.

36. In Hebrew this is Ishmael. See (Genesis 16:11).

37. Genesis 30:1.

38. 1 Samuel 1:4-6.

39. The story of Hagar occurs in Genesis 16:1-16; 21:9-21.

40. Maskil can mean a prayer, a pious meditation or a didactic poem.

41. The first phrase of this psalm is taken from the Authorised Version of the Bible, the second from the Revised Standard Version.

# Select Bibliography

This bibliography contains those books which helped me reflect on my own experience of the desert. They created an atmosphere within which interpretation, understanding and subsequent writing took place.

## 1. THE DESERT WAY

A. M.Allchin, *Solitude and Communion,* Fairacres, 1977.

D. Chitty, *The Desert a City*, Oxford, 1966.

M. Driot, *Fathers of the Desert*, St Paul Publications, 1992.

A. Louth, *The Wilderness of God*, Darton, Longman & Todd, 1991.

J.P. Migne, Relevant volumes in the *Patrologia Graeca* and the *Patrologia Latina*.

T. Merton, *Bread In The Wilderness*, Catholic Book Club, 1953. *No Man Is an Island*, Burns & Oates, 1955, *The Wisdom of the Desert*, New Directions, 1960. *Thoughts In Solitude*, Burns & Oates, 1958.

R.M. Price (Trans), *Cyril of Scythopolis: The Lives of the Monks of Palestine*, Cistercian Publications, 1991.

A. Pronzato, *Meditations on the Sand*,St.Paul Publications, 1982.

N. Russell (Trans),*The Lives of the Desert Fathers*,Mowbray,1980.

H. Waddell (Trans), *The Desert Fathers*, Fontana, 1962.

B. Ward (Trans), *The Sayings of the Desert Fathers*, Mowbrays.


## 2. STORIES AND STORY-TELLING

A.J. Band, *Nahman Of Bratislav: The Tales*, Paulist Press, 1978.

W.J. Bausch, *Storytelling, Imagination and Faith*, Twenty-Third Publications (USA), 1984.

M. Buber, *The Origin and Meaning of Hasidism*, Harper, 1966.

M. Buber, *Hasidism And Modern Man,* Harper, 1966.

N. Corcoran, *The Song of Deeds*, University of Wales Press, 1982.

Y. Eliach, *Hasidic Tales of the Holocaust*, Vintage Books, 1988 .

*The Treasured Writings of Kahlil Gibran*, Castle Books, (USA), 1980.

D.J. O'Leary, *Windows Of Wonder*, Paulist Press (USA), 1991.

A. de Mello, *Wellsprings*, Gujarat Sahitya Prakash, Anand (India), 1982.

C. Nolan, *Under The Eye Of The Clock*. Pan Books. 1987.

J. Ribes, *Parables and Fables For Modern Man*, St Paul Publications, 1990.

I. Shah, *Wisdom Of The Idiots,* Dutton (USA), 1971.

I. Shah, *Thinkers Of The East*, Penguin, 1971.

J. Shea, *Stories of God*, Thomas More Pres (USA), 1978.

J. Shea, *Stories of Faith*, Thomas More Press, 1980.

P. Tribble, *Texts of Terror,* Fortress Press (USA), 1984.

E. Wiesel, *Souls on Fire And Somewhere A Master*, Penguin, 1984.

E. Wiesel, *Four Hasidic Masters*, University of Notre Dame Press, 1 978


## POETRY

J. Ashbery, *Selected Poems*, Paladin, 1987.

C.P. Cavafy, *Collected Poems*, Chatto & Windus, 1979.

W. Cope, *Serious Concerns*, Faber & Faber, 1992.

A. Gregor, *Selected Poems*, Doubleday & Co, 1971.

E. Jennings, *Collected Poems*, Carcanet, 1986.

D. Jones, *The Anathemata*, Faber & Faber, 1972.

R. McKuen, *Come To Me In Silence*, W.H. Allen, 1974.

G. Shaw, *Seeds of Love*, Fairacres, 1978.

R. S. Thomas, *Counterpoint*, Bloodaxe Books, 1990. *Later Poems 1972-1982*, Papermac, 1985. *Selected Poems 1946-1968*, Bloodaxe Books, 1986. *Mass For Hard Times*, Blood Axe Books, 1992.


## SPIRITUALITY

J. Brook, *The School of Prayer,* Harper Collins, 1992.

M. Craighead, *The Sign of the Tree*, Mitchell Beazley, 1979.

B. McGinn et al (Eds), *Christian Spirituality*, vol 1, SCM Press.

R. Nelson, *Kenneth Patchen And American Mysticism*, The University of North Carolina Press , 1984.

J. Puls, *Every Bush Is Burning*, World Council of Churches, 1985.

E. Robinson, *The Language of Mystery*, SCM Press, 1987.

E. Stuart, *Daring To Speak Love's Name,* Hamish Hamilton, 1992.

St Hilda Community, *Women Included*, SPCK, 1991.

The Free Church Of Berkeley, *The Covenant of Peace: A Liberation Prayer Book*, Morehouse-Barlow & Co, 1971.

# THE ABBOT AND THE DWARF

*Tales of wisdom from the desert*

Derek Webster

While on vacation from his university, the author had hoped to write a fairly academic book, but something unplanned happened. Instead of researching in libraries, scholarly institutions and archaeological sites, he felt drawn to solitary places in the desert. From time spent alone in such places were born the stories of Abbot Nicholas and his disciple John the Dwarf. The Abbot and the Dwarf are simple men, poor by worldly standards, yet they try to give something to those they meet. These stories, set against the vivid image of the desert, speak of life and death with a directness that is both refreshing and alarming. *The Abbot and the Dwarf* stands within a rich tradition of fourth century monasticism whose austerity, commitment and wisdom continue to inspire us.

*Derek Webster is an Anglican priest and lectures in the School of Education at the University of Hull. He is also curate at St Peter's parish church, Cleethorpes, in the diocese of Lincoln.*

126 pages      ISBN 085439 416 8      £4.50

# FATHERS OF THE DESERT
*Life and Spirituality*

Marcel Driot

A much needed general introduction to the Fathers of the Desert. It begins by tracing the origin of the practice of retreating to the desert in order to revive a purer and more evangelical form of Christianity away from the cities. This movement, which came to be known as the monastic or ascetic way of life, began in Egypt in the third century and shows why the desert had this irresistible fascination for the men and women of the early Church.

The book acknowledges the Fathers' astounding feats of asceticism, and even more amazing miracles, but rightly gives far greater importance to their *apophthegms* or sayings and anecdotes, the fruit of their years of asceticism, prayer, reflection, reading of the scriptures and the effective practice of charity. This emphasis forms the basis of the book's main message: the men and women who fled the world and lived in the desert were in fact closely involved with the world.

MARCEL DRIOT *is a French monk and hermit.*

126 pages          ISBN 085439 398 6          £5.75

# DESERT AND THE CITY

*A quest for interiority in the footsteps of
the Desert Fathers*

Frère Ivan

*Desert and the City* recounts a personal spiritual experience, one which has as its context the great tradition of the Church and especially of the Desert Fathers.

We live in a world 'full of sound and fury'. Not a week, a day or an hour goes by without bringing its share of wars, violence and indescribable suffering.

The Wisdom of the Desert invites us first and foremost to overcome the evil within ourselves before we become involved in fighting evil in the world, and to drink from the living waters of the Gospel ourselves before we proclaim it to the world. The human heart is the focal point from which transfiguration of history must take place, only the sanctified human being can sanctify the world.

Whether one lives in the Desert or among the masses, co-responsibility in the task of salvation is the same for all. What distinguishes the Desert dwellers is that they show clearly by their lives the depth at which this struggle takes place: the very depths of the heart. For this reason, words from the Desert can have a very real relevance for the City.

126 pages          ISBN 085439 447 8          £6.25

# THE SELF AS FIGHTER

## Shlomo Kalo

*I am myself*, as *I* have always been and eternally will be. There are no words to express this fact; if there were any, *I* would be bound by them in some way. Instead *I* am called to total freedom – to infinite goodness, immortality, lasting happiness, pure love.

Lacking such clear understanding and vision of the *Self*, we try to satisfy our wishes, desires and lusts in the world of people and things. Then, we suffer disappointments which lead us to disillusionment and despair. Eventually, these disappointments and disillusionments turn our attention from the trivial goals we tried to achieve in an illusory world, to the eternal within us. Our awareness grows and induces in us a feeling of relief and joy, like the feeling of relief of someone sunk into a nightmare and yet knows it is only a nightmare.

*The Self as Fighter* proposes to be just a sign post towards that awareness and mastery of the *Self*.

SHLOMO KALO was born in 1928 in Sofia, Bulgaria. From 1962 until his retirement in 1982, he was the director of medical laboratories at the General Health Services (Kupat Holim Klalit) of Rishon le Zion. He is the author of many books, *The Self as Fighter* being the first to be translated into English.

155 pages          ISBN 085439 369 2                    £5.95